ANTON  COAKER

The complete bullocks

A world seen through farmer goggles

Foreword by Professor Ian Mercer CBE

Keep Smiling

Anton Coaker

First published 2013

© Anton Coaker 2013

Published by Anton Coaker
Edited by Sue Viccars, Blackingstone Publishing
Designed by Emily Kingston

By the same author *All the usual bullocks*
wood@anton-coaker.co.uk, www.anton-coaker.co.uk

Acknowledgements

The material in this book has been gleaned from various organisations and publications for which I write, including the National Farmers Union (both in their magazine *British Farmer and Grower* and in a blog on their website), the *Western Morning News* and *Dartmoor Magazine*. Some has appeared in the various Newsletters and Journals of The Galloway Cattle Society, The Belted Galloway Cattle Society and the Riggit Galloway Cattle Society, and some is drawn from private correspondence and emails.

Thanks go to the respective sources for kindly allowing my re-use of material in this publication. Some is previously unpublished.

Some material is reprinted as it was first published, and some has been revised. The organisations listed above do not necessarily endorse or condone the text, views or animal husbandry methods detailed in this book.

Thanks are due to the following:
Sue for patiently and professionally putting my editorial house in order.
Professor Ian Mercer for kindly writing the Foreword.
My lovely family, and even lovelier wife Alison, without whom I would be an utter wreck.
To 'Fate' – or whatever it was – for placing me in such an inspirational place in life.
And to you folk who've encouraged me to keep writing!

Unless otherwise indicated all photographs are by the author or Alison Geen.

Disclaimer

As usual, all of the following is complete fiction. Similarities to actual places, events, people and animals – alive or dead – or animal movements, are entirely coincidental. Almost no offence at all is intended.

British Library Cataloguing in Publication Data
A catalogue record for this book is available from the British Library.

ISBN 978-0-9570953-1-1

Typesetting and origination by Blackingstone Publishing, Moretonhampstead, Devon
Printed in Great Britain by Short Run Press Ltd, Exeter, Devon

FOREWORD

I first stood on the sloping yard of Sherberton farmstead when Anton was — as he describes himself in his earlier memoirs — 'a long-haired teenage, tear-arse motor cyclist'. I was the recently appointed Devon County Conservation Officer (a new idea following European Conservation Year 1970 which Devon decided to celebrate by having a man, rather than a named seat or planting a tree sapling). I had been given responsibility for agriculture and forestry in Devon's planning department. (I had no illusion but that this was because I was not a planner by trade, and had been foisted on the department by the Clerk — nowadays read CEO — and these two subjects would not erode planning purity). Seeking Dartmoor farming know-how (I still lived in the South Hams) I was pointed to Sherberton, by a less-established farmer, to talk to Anton's parents. The Coaker family had been there for 150 years then and Mrs Coaker swiftly gave me the low-down on their brand of hill farming, being a commoner, being a tenant, the Duchy of Cornwall as landlord, grazing its Forest (not a common then, not until 1983) and anything else I remembered to ask about.

Fast-forward 30 years and I found myself asked by the same County Council to conduct a Public Inquiry into the outbreak of Foot and Mouth Disease in Devon. So, I originally learnt from Anton's family the nuts and bolts of Dartmoor hill farming, and much later the agonies the whole of Devon farming suffered during that awful year of 2001. My empathy with Anton's 'Afterword' is therefore total. He declines (openly) to share with the reader his 'Lament' but I have a copy of it and treasure a) his description of his 'lear', the place his Galloways grazed with four sentences each beginning 'They knew…' and b) the quotation from one of (I guess) his heroes, Chief Seattle: 'What is a man without the beasts? If all the beasts were gone, man would die from a great loneliness of the spirit.'

This book is a delight. The realities of hill-farming ups and downs punctuate a life story that is buoyant beyond belief. If Anton Coaker doesn't become one of your heroes after reading this you don't know about heroism.

Ian Mercer CBE
October 2013

The author and son John *Photograph by Agnes Coaker*

INTRODUCTION

After the happy and unexpected success of my first foray into publishing, with the first and now infamous 'Bullocks' book (*All the usual bullocks*) published towards the end of 2011, Sue and I thought we'd have another go. Admittedly, 'success' has been measured by the fact that the mound of stock piled up at home has receded to the point that Alison has granted permission for Volume 2.

Once more, this is a collection of pieces run in papers and magazines, with a smattering of extras which were mostly too fruity for the mainstream.

I have also put together an account of what happened here at Sherberton during the spring of 2001. I've written it pretty much deadpan, just as I recall events. It was very hard to write, and I don't suppose it's much easier to read. Forgive me for including it, and I'll understand if you skip right along when you come to it.

Otherwise, this is pretty much more of the same old nonsense. By its nature, there isn't a plot, which saves us both no end of effort.

The subtitle reflects the fact that I realise my cock-eyed view of the world is framed by my existence up on the hill. While I also run the sawmill, serve on various committees and do a bit of public speaking (where unsuspecting groups pay me a few quid, fill me with provender and ale, so I can repeat all the coarsest jokes I know), I am first and foremost a livestock farmer, still scratching at making a living on a rain-soaked hillside.

I hope you will enjoy reading this book as much as I've enjoyed writing it.

Anton Coaker
Sherberton, October 2013

Red Riggit bull calf *Photograph by David Howard*

BOVINE ASSERTION TRAINING

Over the years, I've subjected various youngsters to a cack-handed form of OJT ('On Job Training') in cattle handling. The jocular reference, in house, is to the 'Bovine Assertion' skill levels achieved. We've seen every level of competence attained in a skill that's hard to explain, and rarely really mastered. In fact, for the benefit of trying to formalise these things, we've now quantified the system humorously applied to operatives hereabouts. I'm sure you'll find it instructive.

GRADE 1 This degree of competence is outlined by the ability to hold a stick and wave it, recognise a docile old South Devon as a cow and make her walk along in front of you. An alternative measure would be the ability to stand in a gap, preventing cattle from escaping through it. Most individuals can usually attain Grade 1 without too much instruction.

I regret to admit that I once failed to ever bring a certain employee up to this level, despite lengthy and careful tuition. In my defence, the individual could hardly count to three twice and get the same answer. He no longer works with livestock.

GRADE 2 A Grade 2 bullock handler is likely of urban upbringing, but has learnt, after gentle reminding, to use his voice when he is driving the 'litmus paper' docile South Devon cow. When she turns her head, he will know to raise the stick as well as his voice. A Grade 2 may not manage to stop her if she walks at him, or likewise stop the group of yearlings advancing at the gap he is blocking.

GRADE 3 We can now start to introduce trickier elements, safe in the assumption that operatives with this grade of skill will actually come in handy.

I would expect a Grade 3 handler to notice his charges are starting to turn their heads, and be able to do something about it. If I were happy with the animal, I would allow a Grade 3 to occasionally handle a particularly dopey

bull. (This is a touchy subject, as the dopiest bull ever will soon pick up when his handler is incompetent/scared. I've known real softies become stroppy when left with a Grade 3 handler for any length of time – in fact, I've known owners of bulls only manage a Grade 3 level themselves, but we won't talk about that.) This grade builds on Grade 2 and should include the ability to look at a group of 10 to 15 cows and notice if one of them is dead/actually calving/walking on three legs (never rely on this assessment, though).

GRADE 4 We're starting to get into realms difficult to achieve from a late start now. Grade 4 bovine assertion skills include being able to spot the individual in the group who is going to turn the rest, and get a stick across its nose before it upsets the apple cart. Equally, you might expect a 'Grade 4' to handle the bull often (without 'Brutus' ever realising that he outweighs his handler by about a tonne), or cast his eye over 40–50 cows and spot the one off on its own/with a festering wound/actually missing. It isn't safe to rely on this inspection either, but hey! you can't be everywhere.

A Grade 4 qualification is, I'm afraid, as high as you're likely to achieve from an adult/urban start. Take comfort that many a full-time farmer would struggle to better this degree of skill – including, I fear, your scribe.

GRADE 5 Due to the esoteric nature of the calibre of Grade 5 cattle handlers, a system of merit stars might be awarded on top of this highest grade. The higher skill levels vary due to circumstance, becoming extremely specialised in each sphere of operation. The finer points of managing milch cows are inevitably different to that of handling semi-feral hill cows, or large numbers of young fattening bulls.

We'll explore the basic Grade 5 requirements, as an indication of the incredible level of intuitive feeling and understanding expected at this level. (Remember, few people are qualified to judge this level.)

A Grade 5 operative has been amongst bovines all of his or her life – and I have known several females quite able to hold a Grade 5 qualification. They likely absorbed their knowledge subconsciously from when they could

walk, at father's or granfer's knee, and been passable Grade 2 cattlemen by the time they started school, and level 3 going on 4 by the time they were in secondary education. Going to agri-college will have had little impact on their proficiency; many have had no further education. By adulthood, they will have mastered ethereal skills that the unenlightened can scarcely grasp. They're never silent in the immediate presence of cattle, but rather murmur to them all the while, identifying the difficult individuals in any group. By habit they will ensure they don't get left with 'Old Grumpy' in the collecting pen, but rather insisted she went on through before she even thought to get arsey. The bull's ears quickly droop when he is in the presence of a Grade 5 handler, knowing he's subordinate but safe. A Grade 5 stockman can be parachuted in to take charge of a stroppy youngster, and re-educate it.

The ability to notice husbandry problems at a glance is a given (although doing this whilst driving past a stranger's herd of cattle at 50mph is something hard to grasp to the uninitiated, but goes on nonetheless).

I recognise theses upper echelons of my profession, if only to aspire to them. I've known candidates for merit stars who display a deep affinity for cattle us mere mortals can barely imagine, and I salute them.

The author watches friend Missus Miggins showing Sherberton Dory

WINTER 2010/2011

What I get up to

As you might know, trying to keep our heads above water, I have what I would prefer you to call a 'rich portfolio of varied business activities'. You might say my commercial interests are 'diverse and fuelled by a keen entrepreneurial spirit'. A less kind analysis of my furtive doings would suggest I'm a conniving little money grabber, with all the less wholesome instincts of a sewer rat. (Thank you, you really are too kind.)

To fill in some of the gaps – or at least some I'm prepared to talk about… You already know I graze a few breeding cows and sheep on Dartmoor with the vague intention that there might be more lives at the end of the year, some of which I could sell. It's a pretty basic way of farming livestock, but I'm probably far too thick to attempt anything more complex. We do 'fatten' a few cattle for direct beef sales, although I'd be the first to admit that skidding them about a hillside until they're big enough is probably not what EBLEX imagine when they're talking about advanced fattening technology.

And there's the sawmill, in which a couple of us unzip local oak logs to produce beams and the like. Again, that's pretty basic stuff – and a refreshingly uncomplicated business compared to how regulated farming has become. I simply have to buy in logs of the right grade and price, convert them into a product the customer desires, and extract payment. I mention this last part, as occasionally a customer fails to grasp that part of proceedings. On this subject, we regularly get cold-called by agencies trying to buy my bad debts. I have to gently explain that as I employ burly blokes with chainsaws and crowbars, who in turn rely on mill customers paying up… well, does the caller really imagine I have difficulty extracting the necessary? The nice Scouse ladies who phone are then perplexed: 'You mean you threaten your customers with chainsaws?' 'Only the ones who don't wish to pay, dear. Goodbye.' And funnily enough, we seldom have on-going trouble in this department.

Beyond the mainstream sawmill and farming activities, however, are a myriad of unlikely lesser goings-on. Obviously, there's the writing, which is handy money in that it can be earned sitting in the dry, with almost no risk of bone-crunching crush injuries, frostbite or traumatic amputations. That's always an attractive consideration to an all-in-bullock wrestler and bandsaw operative.

We also kiln-dry surplus planks from the sawmill for machining into oak flooring and worktops. This involves significant further investment, with a glacial cash turnover. An 'Alan Sugar' type would've given up on the idea years ago, but I like to see every bit of a trunk used if I can.

As well as timber – and in case I get bored – I also trade in a bit of granite, keeping a few thousand tonnes handy. This is another fairly straightforward job, albeit involving heavy plant and machinery costs, a steady nerve and patience. (In fact, I could do with an upturn in the building trade, if you could mention it to the Chancellor when you see him next.)

Back on the farm, we also sell a few hide rugs. It takes a bit of care to raise and present bullocks with well-marked hides in clinker-free condition, and there're still plenty of slip-ups along the way. Curing them takes time and money, and carrying a working stockpile all racks up.

Then there are a few Dartmoor ponies about the place. Sadly, with no trade in 'Dartmoor pony salami', they are worth very little – ironically, the 'do-gooders', with their cockeyed idea of 'saving' the ponies, have almost destroyed the herds of wild mares. I suppose, apart from one or two notable and realistic exceptions, their charitable concerns are at least giving some of them profitable employment, and allow a few of the 'saved' colts to live out an extended existence in a 'sanctuary'. For my own mares, which are pedigree, and live running free across vast acreages, we sell a handful of higher-priced youngsters quite well, with surplus colts to go straight into the food chain.

Another minor earner is small amount of bull/ram hire. Apart from straight hire jobs – for which I keep a motley collection of obliging well-mannered old boys – there is a peculiar niche market, whereby, if I've bred/ obtained a particular bull calf, I sometimes lend it out to trusted chums to rear on, on the simple logic that it's getting bigger on someone else's grub.

One left here as a 10-month-old calf, and is currently circulating a nearby county doing sterling work within a select community. The last I heard of him, he weighed about five times what he did when he left me. Ideal.

With these various interests in mind, we set sail on a jolly north last week. The beloved needed a break, so we tied in a few pick-ups and drops, to give us an excuse to get away.

First off was delivering a Dartmoor pony to Scotland – the lengths we have to go just to get rid of them! Then, after a couple of nights' stopover with some friends amongst heather-clad mountains, collected up a bull calf or two to head south again. To my beloved's consternation I had also organised to meet a pal in a supermarket car park by Carlisle, to pick up some rare burr elm as well – after all, there was a space on the back of the trailer, and why go all that way without making full use, eh?

I'm seldom bored.

South Devon in the snow

Gyp's day out

'Dad' was up and about early today. I didn't know what was on, but he was loading some old cows into the stock box before dawn. I took up my station under the ramp, and this time I remembered not to bite his fingers as he reached down to close the tailgate. He gets quite cross when I forget myself. Sometimes, his plastic pipe jabs unexpectedly under the ramp, making me yelp! As he clambered into the Landrover, he nodded at the back, saying the magic words 'Go on then urchin, jump in', so I leapt in the back, and we pulled out of the yard gate.

As we trundled down the lane in the first grey light, I snapped at those pesky trees beside the road, which always try to ambush us as we drive past. I gave one quite a nip this time, really scaring it - so much in fact that it ran away, almost dragging me from the truck. (For some reason, Dad disapproves of this as well. He really is a spoilsport about some things.)

Dad and me *Photograph by Agnes Coaker*

After quite a long time, we arrived at a place I didn't recognise. There was a big building, with old cows being unloaded at one end, and steaming trolleys of hides and innards being wheeled out of a side door. It smelled fantastic, but Dad shut me in the cab while he unloaded. I ran to and fro across the seats all the while, in case any of the paperwork he'd left needed scrunching up a bit. The old misery didn't seem to like this either.

As well as the lovely smells permeating the site, I noticed a shining healthy game cockerel, strutting about the place like he owned it. I'd have scrunched him as well, but Dad wouldn't let me, saying something about it being right and proper to see such a bird.

Off we went again. It was raining all the while, but that never dampens my enthusiasm for going driving. It was raining so much, in fact, that rivers were coming out over their banks as we went along. We stopped to admire one, where Dad ate a bite, tearing a crust off for me. Gosh, I'm a lucky dog. We eventually arrived at a farm far from home, where a lady I didn't know greeted the Boss, and they went off to admire her cattle. I jumped out to admire her collection of spaniels, one of which needed some special attention, if you know what I mean. Somehow though, these days, I don't seem to be able to investigate these things properly. In fact, ever since 'Mum' took me off to meet the nice man in the green coat, who smelled of disinfectant and made me all sleepy, I know there's something I should be doing, but can't quite recall exactly what it is. I'm sure it'll come back to me in a bit.

After the humans had eaten again - beggars never gave me anything - we set off once more, leaving the trailer behind. First we went to see some nice people to look at something called a 'walnut tree'. Dad can't have liked it very much, because he shook his head a lot, and kept his hands firmly in his pockets all the while. I don't know what was wrong with it, apart from

its bits of concrete poured in the rot holes, iron rods driven right through the splits, and a length of chain grown into the bark. (I heard him say something about 'More ironwork than Gimli's effing underpants'). I marked it when no one was looking.

Back on the road, a couple of those strange creatures passed us. You know, the ones with a wheel at each end, and a man in a helmet in the middle. I love them, and almost got one as it screamed past. It was so exciting I widdled a bit.

Then we went up onto some moorland I didn't recognise at all, into yet another farmyard. Here, while he went off looking at some more cattle, I had a good old sniff round. I met a very doddery old collie, and an unusually amiable Patterdale - the little black hellhounds are usually like shrunken snarling Rottweilers. It was a lovely old farmyard, with all manner of fowls rooting about, and lines of healthy-looking cattle stood eating in the buildings. A lot like home in fact, only with fatter cows and less junk. Dad seemed very impressed, but he soon called me back to the truck, and we set off yet again.

I'm surprised the truck still had any energy (I'd be exhausted from running so far in one day), but it still seemed eager, and soon found its way back to where we'd left the stock box. While Dad loaded up a bull I vaguely recognised, I went off to see that spaniel again. By now it was getting dark, and we headed off onto one of those big roads, where the bushes are all too far back to bite, so Dad allows me to travel in the front with him. Eventually, we turned off up a track, and let the bull out in the dark. He trotted straight in amongst the cows, and seems to remember what he's meant to do much better than I can. Lucky blighter.

And then it was home again for tea. Wow Dad, that was fun... when can we go again?

Translated from 'Grrr, bark, woof woof' by the wonders of modern science

Saving the world

With the week bringing wet snow, verging to sleet, most days so far – weather that sorts the wheat from the chaff up here – I'm sorry, but I'm struggling to be my usual jovial self just at the moment. You'll just have to take it as it comes, or move smartly along if you prefer.

I've lately been overly exposed, as you might well have, to various 'save the world' schemes. To alleviate global warming, rising sea levels, and the plight of the 'Greater Crested Greenpiece', we're being coerced to put solar panels on the roof of the forage harvester, catch the methane seeping from the nether ends of our cows, and adopt a plague of locusts. So it all seems, anyway. And indeed, like a good little bunny, I'm looking at various routes by which I can do my bit. I'm even involved with an ambitious carbon-capturing project. I do care, I really do. As rough as the conditions outdoors have treated me of late, I know that I live, wastefully, in comparative luxury.

Unfortunately though, when the short daylight hours and low temperatures weigh heavily, the niceties of what's being mentioned in the media kind of pales. The realities seem to be something we won't talk about (and certainly not in front of the children – a metaphor loaded with irony, considering that it's their future we're fooling with).

While we're fiddling about, Rome is ablaze, briefly flaring off 100 million years' worth of fossil fuels. I'm idly crunching the carbon numbers as I trundle out to feed some cattle, in the tractor – I'm pretty sure I'm producing better than a tonne of beef or lamb per tonne of fossil fuels used, although it's harder to know how much is used up- and downstream – while, somewhere above the leaden clouds, the sky is crisscrossed with vapour trails left by people on absolutely meaningless journeys.

While I've been giving consideration to all the little bits of consumption – which add up to such a huge rate of expenditure – to grow food, governments still desire 'growth' (ie ever greater rates of consumption), and people living modern lives in the developed world have the jaw-dropping front to talk about 'sustainability'.

The grim reality is that we're seemingly hardwired to go on behaving as if there'll be no tomorrow. None of us is prepared to give up the easy life and endless toys – well, no one I see out of my windows at least – do spare me if you are that sainted individual.* I suppose none of us wants to act unilaterally. Why should I give up my comforts, when the next man might not?

It strikes me as pretty peculiar that there isn't any talk about what's actually going to happen when it's time for the party to end. Perhaps there's just too much propaganda floating about. You've got to assume that various lobbies have an immense effect on what is aired, corporate and political interests being what they are.

Some things are inescapable, yet brushed right out of sight under the carpet. We rely on food and, increasingly, fuels and fibres, grown with the aid of fertiliser squidged out using natural gas (and no, I don't know how it works, just that it is so).

The supplies of the raw materials needed to continue doing this are in the hands of fewer, and less reliable, hands every year. I find the idea of depending on, for instance, Mr Putin for the raw materials to grow our essentials distinctly disturbing.

Sorry, don't mean to sound so glum. I'm sure my mood will lighten as evenings pull out.

*As it goes, Alison and I just about never fly, reckoning it must be about the most irresponsible way to get around. In fact, I don't think any of the kids have seen the inside of a plane. When it's time, fine, they can go see the world, but not to lie on a beach for a week. Friends are astonished, and uncomfortable, when we give our reasons, but I don't see anything unusual in it whatsoever.

Egbert's heifers

I think it's high time we infused another character into my scribblings.

We're going to call him 'Egbert', for no other reason than it sounds as foolish as he is.

I won't bother to introduce him further, but shall simply start feeding in stories from his troubled farming career. (Like you and I, he is far from perfect, but he

is merely better at ease with his imperfections, and more ready to share them.*)

This Egbert fellow grazes a few heifers on the meadow flats near to the river locally. When pressed, he admits that he knew this is a chancy thing to do, but it was also a handy spot to put a little bunch away from the bull, and in about 20 years' usage he'd never had any bother there.

One stormy night, however, a colossal rainstorm hit the moors upstream, and the following morning Egbert found all four heifers gone. Now he beat himself up something dreadful about it, knowing only too well that he could have averted this calamity, but what's done is done. The watermark, at the lower end, was found to be about 12 feet above the normal level. Panicked, in the dark, they stood no chance.

The owner of the meadows was almost as despondent as old Egbert, and word flashed round the parish, to be met with deep regret wherever such news means anything.

Egbert decided against opening a bottle that night (although he admitted to being pretty tempted), but did think to send telegrams to those farmers next downstream, warning them to look out for the flotsam. He was now hoping that if they'd gone, better they'd gone far enough to become a hazard to shipping. (Shortly downstream, the river enters a steep-sided oak-clad ravine, hundreds of feet deep and several miles long.)

Sure enough, a call came the next day. One of the poor creatures was found hung up in a riverside tree, not far downstream, adjacent to the next farm along. She'd swim no further.

Being that the site was frequented by several hardy ramblers, Egbert 'phoned a friend' (a discreet professional with a sharp knife and a couple of hooks, who Egbert assures me is a gent in every way). Late that afternoon, the two of them set off down into the steep-sided valley where this animal had come to rest to 'tidy up'. On the way, Egbert couldn't help but notice that there were a couple of heifers of the same breed, grazing peacefully in the nearest of his neighbours' fields. Most locals keep this breed though, so it didn't signify much. Egbert kept his mind on the job in hand.

When, however, the neighbour came down over to see how the operation was going, he admitted he had no heifers this side, and went rushing off to

have a look. He was soon back with news that two of Egbert's heifers had indeed escaped the river, and had scrawled up out of the rough to safety.

I believe Egbert allowed himself a brief snifter when he got in that night. One more to find.

The following day then brought a call from the next neighbour down. He rents the little farm opposite, which hangs on the edge of the valley as it plunges into the ravine. It's the last farmable ground for several miles downstream. He'd come out to feed his stock, to find the last of Egbert's missing heifers pacing up and down the fence against where his cattle were lying. She was looking a bit wild-eyed and lost, but was soon shut safe in the man's handling pen. He was pretty pleased to be able to make the call, and Egbert was even more pleased to get the message.

How that heifer got across that raging river in the dark that night, no one knows. It would have been 100 feet wide, 15 feet deep, and fairly roaring along. I hear Egbert had to have a pretty big snort that night. I'm told the three survivors are now known as 'the swimmers'.

As a brief coda, Egbert admitted to me that he and his boy were sitting by the fireside one wintry night soon after, watching some damp old beech logs splutter and hiss (not much else to do those long winter nights in the hills). 'Look Dad,' says Egbert Jnr, 'there's sap boiling out the end of that one.' Being an inquisitive lad, he grabbed a handy scrap of bendy plastic, scraped up some of this sap and had a taste. Egbert tried some too, and they agreed it tasted of beech wood, and smoke. Egbert suggested it also had a hint of earwax. 'Why's that then Dad?' asked Jnr. 'Cos yon scrap of plastic is half the tag I cut from the ear of that drowned heifer, son.'

Being that Egbert Jnr is getting the kind of upbringing so missing from many a household, he merely observed that 'It's OK Dad, we know what she'd a-died from.'

*Persons wishing to find this awful man Egbert – and a number of folk might want to have sharp words with him – may very well seek him propping up the bar at various isolated hostelries, or possibly leaning on his stick watching the cattle judging at an

out-of-the-way little show, or perhaps chewing the fat with some equally scruffy old cronies at a store sale. I should advise them, however, that their enquiries are likely to fall on stony ground. He's a pretty elusive chap, and his cronies are devils for giving nosey enquirers the runaround.

Probably better – given that he is a man with a tremendous thirst – leave a drink with me to give him when I see him next.

SPRING 2011

Planning the summer diary

I don't know if it has ought to do with threats of privatisation, but there seem to be some problems within the postal service. See, the summer season's outings are being organised, sifted from various schedules and invitations, which drop through the letterbox alongside the bills about now. As well as entry forms to fill in for the Veteran In Hand Rick Building classes at the Drizzlecombe District Show, and the hotly contested Junior Clear Round Clydesdale Jumping Challenge at the same, there's a kind invitation to judge the Ridden Terrier classes at the 122nd Stoggy Butt Country Fair. There is also, of course, a load of extraordinarily optimistic invoices and reminders, which have been neatly 'filed'.

These have to be filed away, as amongst other items of post that notably don't seem to have turned up are several promised RPA payments, and unexpected solicitors' letters from the executors of long-lost great uncles, asking for confirmation that they can forward substantial bequests. Admittedly, a Mr Joseph Mdogo, of Lagos, has offered to send me some money, but I smelled a rat when he asked for my bank details. He hasn't come back to me since I asked him if he could send me the handling fee, in cash, for processing his letter.

Also mysteriously absent is a request to serve as Steward-in-Chief to the Chipping Huddesley Ale Tasting Festival, along with an invitation to judge the Sunnycombe Bay Ladies Beach Volleyball competition. Worse still, a missive from the Glen McSporran Malt Whisky Distillers Association, demanding my immediate attendance to settle a dispute in the blending of some 15-year-old casks, complete with first-class rail tickets and reservations at the (five-star) Loch Gloaming Hotel, seems to have become unaccountably lost in the post.

I feel very let down, and must take it up with the Postmaster General.

Helping the boy show his pet lamb at Widecombe Fair *Photograph by Jessica Martin*

Fly and Becks

With the bantams laying full blast, there's more eggs coming into the house than we know what to do with. Polly did leave a bucketful – yes, a bucketful – on the kitchen floor last week. Alison's thicko deerhound noticed this, and by the time I happened along she was halfway down the bucket. (This didn't seem to have much effect on her, but then nothing stirs her much one way or the other.)

There's generally more eggs the last week or two, since two of the elderly collies have left us in quick succession. Both Fly and Becks were fond of egg hunting. A favourite spot for a couple of hens to lay has been under a bench in the outbuilding Becks slept in, so she hardly had to get up mornings, just wait for breakfast to be laid. (The aforementioned bucketful was retrieved when Joe and I cottoned on what might be a side effect of Beck's demise.)

Fly did at least go doddering out and about, carefully noting where henny-penny was flustering about. I watched her one morning. She followed a black banty into the garden, trailing by a few minutes. Sticking her snout in where the fowl was doing her thing, she realised she was a bit early, so she made her apologies, and politely retired to wait until her snack was ready. I think the eggs kept her going these last few months.

Fly was born in '96, to my favourite bitch. I inherited the bitch line from my Dad, who bought the original Fly from a certain Mr Hodge, of Okehampton, nearly 50 years ago. This one was fairly inbred, and I wouldn't ordinarily have kept a pup from the litter. However, her sire was a dear old dog we'd had forever, who been run over in his late teens before the bitch whelped. We never thought he was up to the job – perhaps that's why he got run over. Anyway, I decided to keep a pup in his memory. He fulfilled, as far as I could tell, just about every male relative role, although Fly grew up as normal as any of my motley hounds. Her mother Peach was also into double figures when it all happened. She was about the kindest-natured brown bitch I've had, who got under the wheels of the Landrover while out moving sheep, when the pup was hardly old enough to wean. Given this, I had to keep Fly, didn't I?

She proved to be only a second-rank working dog, although she was happy to come along and play what part she could. The only ill effects of her somewhat shallow gene pool was a tendency to have a bit of a fit when she'd done more than two or three hours. You'd miss her, look back along the track, and there she'd be, lying twitching. After the first time or two, we just left her to it. About 20 minutes later, she'd catch up, albeit with a bit of a list to starboard.

She went on to live a long and happy life, although I stopped letting her come to the moor when I realised I was having carry her through the worst of the rough. We never let her breed, although I don't think she would've. Of late, she's been pretty deaf, and seems to have learnt to lip-read. This became a bit difficult when she started losing her sight as well, but she tottered about the yard, nicking eggs right until she went to sleep under the box bush in the garden, and didn't wake up.

Becks had different luck. She was named after the events of Layland's 40th birthday party, where a teenage pal experimented how much bottled lager – of that name – he could contain in one go. He fell at the tenth we think, hardly seeing sunset, although we did name a pup in his honour. I can't tell you about events that transpired much later in the evening, after the lightweights had slid below the straw bales. Suffice that I didn't feel as comfortable trying to name a dog 'Case of whisky and the improbable wheelbarrow recovery position'.

Becks was a shaggy-coated black cousin to Fly, who scored about 7/10 as a worker. She was useful if not outstanding, and has bred some excellent pups by my top dog Gyp – preferring to whelp in a burrow dug under a hedgebank. But then, at 12, she developed what seems to have been a tumour in her sinus. When it erupted, mucus oozed down her cheek in a most unpleasant manner. Two of the practice vets had seen her, and concurred that there wasn't much to be done if she was comfortable. I tried bathing it, but she hated that, so I let her have a few more weeks snuffling for bantam eggs about the yard and looking horrible. Complaints were coming in, so I pulled the plug the same week as Fly went on.

And so… there's eggs everywhere now. Another omelette, kids?

Trip hazard

I ran into Egbert the other day, leaning on a rusty dung spreader at a collective machinery sale. For the uninitiated, this is a springtime ritual where whole farming communities turn out to exchange one piece of worn-out junk for another. It's a bit like the Hobbits and their mathoms. I've long suspected that if you chose to peel away the sale tickets of Hackett & McSprocket (auctioneers and agents to the gentry), you'd find someone else's ticket below – or possibly just another H&M one from a previous year.

Some of the dysfunctional bits of ironwork ('It worked the last time it was used…') have slipped so far into the realms of antiquity that they've become collectible without anyone realising. I made such an observation to Egbert, who nodded that this was the case. Indeed, he's discovered that at least two of his tractors are now increasing in value once more, having been sliding into the liability zone since some time before the miners' strike. He assures me he wouldn't part with either of them though, being as they seldom break down, and when they do he can generally fix 'em with a lump hammer. In fact, Egbert reckons another benefit of their being collectible is that there seem to be spares easily available again.

We then got on to what else has been happening in the old rogue's life. It was a pleasant sunny day, and as the novice element of the crowd surged to and fro, keeping abreast of the auctioneer and watching the trade, old hands like Egbert and I lingered to chat, enjoying the proper function of the occasion. Obviously conversation becomes a bit difficult when the crowd moves along the row, and seethes around the bale trailer you're leaning against. The chap with the gavel tends to interrupt conversation, but he soon moves on with his disciples.

So what has Egbert been up to? Well, like many of us, he tries to catch up with cutting surplus attachments off youngstock in the spring. Once the grass has come, they'll be harder to get hold of, see. Whilst wrestling with some of the unfortunate patients in the rusting crush – much patched and tied up with bale cord – his vet politely speculated that the horns and testicles strewn about the race were becoming a trip hazard. Were they entered on the risk assessment form, she speculated? (I hear the vet's practice saves visits to Egbert for recently qualified youngsters, as some kind of rite of passage, or punishment for piquing a senior partner in some way.)

Thinking about it, I rather get the impression that Egbert's operation lies somewhere outside the paperwork which burdens us all nowadays. I haven't checked, but it may very well be that his farm is merely a blank space on official maps, 'white' land labelled only *There be dragons here*. An unlikely rumour surfaced last autumn that an inspector of some kind did once find his way that far into the backwoods. I can't vouch for the accuracy of this story, and Egbert would never give a straight answer to such a question, leave alone admit what might befall a Government inspector out there.

Mind, I did notice when I last passed that some of Egbert's cattle were sporting an eartag or two, which would indicate that the 21st century is within sight – if only by use of his old-fashioned telescope, admittedly. Even more up to date, I'm told he was spluttering into his ale, and blaspheming something dreadful the other night, at the bar of the Fellmongers Arms. It turned out Mrs Egbert – a very tolerant woman indeed – had enquired about these here 'lectronic tags for the sheep', and reported the implications and cost back to himself (being considered only via the telescope).

On the subject of his sheep, I understand Egbert has just about finished lambing, not liking to make a start until the weather is relatively safe, even up on his storm-blasted ridge. He says the boy has been helping him lamb the ewes again, during the school holidays – he's a solid-built lad, interested in livestock far more than tractors, and is the apple of Egbert's eye. What will happen when the school somehow allows the Easter holidays to miss Egbert's lambing dates remains unknown, but it won't be pretty. Anyway, the lad was out most mornings and evenings, helping catch ewes that needed sorting out, and ringing and marking lambs (and learning some new words into the bargain). One evening, while holding the jug as his Dad milked out a ewe that had buckets of colostrum, Egbert realised the little blighter was in fact drinking the stuff as fast as Dad was stripping it into the transfer cup. Edgar cussed the lad roundly. Had he forgotten that double up beside the fence, which needed topping up?

Still, as Egbert assures me now, at least the lad shouldn't get pulpy kidney.

Haltering

Since we last spoke, someone from a Government department I'd better not name asked if I'd do him a favour. Why, I said, what is this favour? Well, he replied, he had to interview some 'customers' to get feedback for his biggest boss. And what exactly do you want of me, I asked... to be on holiday on such-and-such a date, so as to make myself unavailable for interview? No, no, he assured me. She needs to hear it as it is. (It was to be a 'talking heads' video presentation. I was confused – 'This is not my beautiful house, this is not my beautiful wife. How did I get here?')

So, after two hours in make-up, and an hour in the hairdressing salon, I was 'ready for my close-up, Mr DeMille'. To set the scene, I sat at the diagonal feeder in front of the weaned Galloway calves. As I answered questions – fully and frankly I hope – a rather smart Belt heifer kept coming into frame, or at least, her long curly tongue did, hooking wisps of hay from my hand. I hope it came out well, and that the good lady enjoyed the show. Autographs are available for a modest fee.

More interestingly, the heifer in question is set to make a guest appearance at the Bath & West, as is one of her Riggit cousins – they are rather more photogenic than I am. Stockman Joe is itching to drag a Galloway or two round a ring, so we're letting him have a day out.

I suppose someone better remind Joe to get a halter on these heifers before the day! I did sell a yearling Riggit bull to a pal this time last year, who asked if we'd halter it before we loaded it. Fine we agreed, chortling. Then, expecting Jeremy to be dragged all round the yard by a young bull raised far out on the Forest, he led the youngster down from the crush, through the yard and up into his trailer with just about no fuss whatsoever. Hmm, it's as easy as that is it? See photo, taken three minutes after halter first applied.

I suppose I'd better shuffle off and see what the bovines are up to.

Jeremy takes delivery of Border Reiver

Lambing winding down

Lambing is winding down, as my ovine ladies get to the end of their first cycle. Only one group has been tardy, and after I'd mentally put a bullet in the tup – a real beaut, by a nine-year-old sire – I remembered we let him have first go, alone, at 120 ewes. Perhaps I'll forgive him. The 'B' team rams were thrown in after a cycle, and the results are just coming through now. The Cheviots are mostly down to the two-tooth first-timers, who generally tup later in a group. The rest have lambed an absolute treat. It must be the easiest lambing I've ever had. Lovely strong lambs, with viable twins, and thankfully none of those useless triplets. I used to chase higher lambing percentages, but the years have rubbed that stupidity off. The reality is that the moment I have to put any time to an outfit, the labour bill wipes out any chance of profit.

Three or four calves are appearing each day now, so there's no let-up. I'm still covering miles every day, craving sleep and/or deep-fried fatty and salty food. Falling into the comfy chair means my eyes will close in about four minutes flat.

So far I've managed to get tags in most of the calves as I've gone, although it is a bit of a white-knuckle ride when they start bawling, and half a dozen Aunties come roaring over. They crab round – clockwise generally – like Injuns galloping round the settlers' wagons drawn up in a circle, bellowing like things demented. It does wonders for your 'speed castration' and tagging technique, but is still so much better done first off. Wrestling with them later, half grown, is a recipe for scraped knuckles and various contusions.

The only worrying episode so far was when an especially testy member of the 'Doreen' cow family calved next to a footpath on Good Friday. Streams of ramblers and Ten-Tors-practising kids went past her. One group of visitors even sat on a nearby rock and watched her pop the calf out. They stopped by the yard to say how nice it was to watch this marvel of nature. By the time I got round to her that evening, her eyes were out on stalks, nostrils flared and snorting, as she guarded her little black treasure. I declined to try and give it an earring – it was a boy as well, and I was never going to get a ring on him, and escape alive. I tiptoed away, hoping she took it off into the undergrowth before morning.

Checking a Beltie calf *Photograph by Agnes Coaker*

They have been a strange group of cows to work with, the Doreens. They arrived here after FMD having been shunted around a bit, although they originated from a very good source. For the first couple of years they were so wild I could barely handle them, although they leared* very well and settled down to breeding regularly. The first crop of daughters were so maze** I killed the lot, and suspected that I'd have to breed the strain right out for my own safety. I sent one or two of the worst to the 'happy retirement home' for old cows, and sold another one in a job lot to a pal. He mentioned this, next time we met... 'Yere, Anton, that black 'un was a bit fruity!' (In my defence, Andrew, I did try and persuade you to choose a different cow.)

But as the years went on they calmed down, and subsequent progeny learned better manners. Slowly, gentle handling got several of them quiet enough to get a hand on their backs, and I'm even allowed to tag newborns of some now – they still come eye to eye, and snort a bit, but it's doable. Several of their daughters and granddaughters are much loved and biddable cattle, and I've kept a couple of very useful bulls from the line. The beautiful pair of Riggit heifers that Alison

Bunning shows both sprung from that source, although you'd never guess (see page 39). Conclusive proof that it can be nurture as well as nature.
* *accustomed and acclimatised to living on a particular area of open hill*
** *mad/stupid*

And yes, I did get involved in making out the wildfire, up behind Fernworthy over Easter. It has become something of a hill-farmers' social event now, turning out when the common catches fire. It looks suspiciously like a camper's stove started the fire, but the swift response of rangers, fire service, and us peasants soon had it under control. I was one of three who responded from the South Quarter, and got to spend a pleasant hour or two swinging a beater beside Kenny Watson, and the lovely Rachael (East Quarter) above Teignhead, as Colin Friend (West Quarter) floundered about in the mire, trying to refill the water tank strapped to his quad. To be fair to Colin, and the other quad-mounted 'fogging' outfits working further along the firefront, once they've found some water they certainly make very short work of putting it out. Hopefully a bit of rain will have eased this, and other situations.

Trip to Avebury

Calving is slowing down – perhaps the boys needed a breather – and feeding has almost stopped. This allows me to take, nay, whisk Alison off for a romantic night away from kids and worries. An overnight bag was packed, and while herself was parish councilling one evening, I tracked down a rather swish room for the night, up on the chalk, in Wiltshire. Some of you have already smelt the rodent in this, knowing what a tight wad I am. And sure enough, our chariot for this jaunt was once more the truck, loaded with outbound timber… Well, seems silly not to take advantage of an excuse to get out of the county for a night.

This time, it was another delivery for our refined gardener pal, David Howard (V.I.G.). He's landed a job restoring a neglected old walled garden for a telly show, and kindly asked us to supply a load of red cedar for the raised beds. The site was the big old house in a place called Avebury.

Once we'd been filmed offloading – long time in make-up for me again – and we'd snaffled a feed from the caterers, Alison and I sneaked off to look around. The rambling 500-year-old house is fantastic, if neglected, with oak panelling and stone mullions of a pretty spectacular order. I didn't catch all the history of its origins, although it almost certainly involved someone with a bigger sword than anyone else nearby. A gravestone in the churchyard next door indicates there were titles involved.

Out in the yard, an oak-framed, thatched threshing barn was of a stature to impress even me. Then it was on through to the main attraction, the prehistoric element to Avebury.

The camera never lies…

I've long wanted to see stone ring at Avebury, with its vast circular ditch and mound, lying right across the more 'modern' village and containing a ring of colossal boulders. These might not be as regular as Stonehenge, but are nonetheless equally arresting. Obviously, you have to elbow your way through throngs of foreign tourists and purple-cloaked New Agers, but it is well worth it. Just to the south is the massive conical man-made Silbury Hill, 120 feet high and covering five acres.

Academics still debate the purpose of both sites, but as far as Silbury goes, I don't. The moment it hove into view, I knew from the very bottom of my toes that it's a statement. It says 'I am here.' It's reckoned to have been constructed 4700 years ago, using 120,000 tonnes of material, which would have taken hundreds of men some years to pile up. I don't know who drove the project, but I'd bet he wasn't a shrinking violet, and his flint axe would've been big and sharp.

For the record, I feel no connection whatsoever with whoever it was that piled up all that dirt, or raised the nearby pebbles. Like all of those monuments up on the chalk, and the echoes of the men who built them, they remain alien to me. If I catch the whiff of their presence, frankly, it gives me the creeps.

I can, however, relate to the more recent population, who grow a lot of corn, and milk a few cows. Now I should say I mean the extant descendants of the incoming Saxons and their dark-haired predecessors, for this was the heart of the kingdom of Wessex. Did they absorb those earlier tribes, or squeeze them out? I don't know.

Sadly, they too are now being pushed out in turn, by yet another wave of invaders. For a huge wash of urban refugees, from the Southeast, is filling all the surrounding villages with Volvos and BMWs, drinking lattes and downsizing their middle-class lives.

In the village just up the way, where we pitched up at our lodgings for the night, the contrast was stark. After settling into our room, we meandered down the street to pick up a newspaper. The postmaster was very much a local (and a lovely fellow), as was the mum who stopped her car in the street, and got out to pull grass from the verge for the kids' pet rabbit. I discovered she could trace her family in the village for 150 years. However, everyone else we came into contact with had the air of suburbia about them. No toddlers played in their immaculate manicured gardens, no skateboarding youths slouched in their expensive cul de sacs. It was a bit odd.

The following morning we parked the truck up on the nearby ridge, to admire one of the many 'white horses' carved into the thin turf, and have a meander along the ridge-top footpath. Curiously, there we found evidence of where the elusive local youngsters do hang out. In a beech copse on the side of the hill, overlooking this strange community, there were the remains of several bonfires, surrounded by drifts of empty beer cans. I daresay the cans will be archaeology themselves one day. Perhaps the interpretation will speculate on some kind of fertility rite, and I rather hope that this is the case.

Calving goes apace

Calving goes apace, differing from lambing chiefly in the volume of amniotic fluid. Instead of a half-pint bag warning of an impending new ovine arrival, a cow can, should you find yourself the wrong place, shower you with gallons.

There are inevitably one or two hiccups. One South Devon was licking a stillborn calf first thing one morning. She's had two or three calves previously, raised without problems, and gave no impression of having had a difficult calving. The calf wasn't swollen, overly big, or wrong in any way – well, other than it was as dead as a dead thing. I left her loving it, in case we needed a spare mum later.

Sure enough another cow, with a strapping three-to-four-day-old bull calf, seemed to have an overly full udder, as happens when the grass starts to come. No worries, Joe could milk her out, so the calf could get on top of things again. Oh no he couldn't. He soon discovered she had, quite out of the blue, mastitis in all four quarters. No wonder she was swollen. It didn't seem to be upsetting her, beyond the obvious, although

I very much doubted she'd be rearing the calf by the time we got her sorted. So Joe nipped out and skinned the stillborn, and we neatly fitted its skin onto the spare calf's back, tucking his legs into slots cut at each corner. Then he was given to the mother of the dead calf. If it's going to work this trick generally works like a charm, and can be done with sheep, cattle or ponies. (I don't know what else it works on, but do let me know!)

Anyway, yon cow sussed straight off that it wasn't her calf, and would only let it suck with someone stood over her for a few days. She's dopey enough though, so it'll come right in a minute.

Another calving saw a two-year-old White Galloway heifer, who absolutely should not have been in calf, having a premature calf. It looked pretty tight in there, so we fetched Chris the vet to her. He made it look easy enough, with a bit of time, and an extra rope behind the calf's head. The heifer was fine, and never went down. Sadly, the calf was just at the wrong stage to survive – perhaps eight months – and its lungs wouldn't function. Still,

Tiddly Wee (see overleaf)

now the heifer can grow on before she should be breeding. The jury is still out on the identity of the sire of the (black) calf. There was an incident with Tony's Charolais late in the summer, where the yearlings were at grass last year, but it sure wasn't a Charolais. Immaculate conception I expect.

Curiously, premature calves can survive when delivered even earlier.

We once had a South Devon cow raise a calf that came into this world the size of a spaniel, with a coat like velvet. It was so small it used to stand right under mother, and reach up to feed. Other than initially giving her a bit of shelter indoors, in bad weather, we never had to help her along at all. The cow had had twins previously, and I looked carefully for another calf to match 'Tiddly Wee', but never found a trace of it. I've always suspected that she was half a double, but the other was absorbed or miscarried earlier. This might've left her a 'freemartin', unable to breed, for such is sometimes the fate of heifers born as a twin to a bull calf. This is something to do with the hormones in the cow, during pregnancy. I've never really understood how it works, despite repeated patient careful explanation from my betters. Obviously, when I sold her, I admitted this possibility, in case the purchaser should wish to keep her for breeding. Happily, as far as I know, she grew on and did breed.

Speaking of twins, we've a pair on another South Devon this week. Without checking the records, I'm pretty sure the cow is a close relative to the above-mentioned outfit. Such fecundity is very much an inheritable trait, although not one I'm particularly keen on. The chances of a cow raising a 'double' up here, without significant assistance, are slim. This outfit is fine at the time of writing, but only because the cow is shut in 15 acres, and can't wander off leaving one behind.

To be fair, I have had cows successfully get two calves going out on the veldt, able to recall where they've left them both. Famously, an argument touched off when a big black cow, 'Fiona', calved in the undergrowth, only breaking cover to come to the feeder. Joe was convinced she had a black Belted calf, but when I was feeding, I was sure it was a solid dun. I told Joe he needed to get on down to Specsavers. Alison finally settled the dispute with the aid of the binoculars, explaining that Fiona had two calves at foot one morning, one of each colour.

Fostering red and black

Still on calving, it's brought the usual smattering of problems. Chasing calves around the gorse bushes, trying to attach some eartags and a rubber ring, then being chased back the other way by cows anxious to prevent such defilement of their newborn babies.

Then a Beltie was found loving another stillborn, while a few fields away the aforementioned South Devon was only just remembering she had twins to keep together. This one didn't look as likely. The Belts are no fools, and not always given to docility in close quarters when newly calved. Well, it had to be worth a try. So we fetched them all in, and while Joe milked out the bursting Beltie – who remained quite civil – in the crush, I skinned her calf. Bless me, as we fitted the South Devon twin – picking the weedier, which kept getting left behind – into the skin it bawled a bit. The Belt, facing away from us in the crush, answered immediately (she'd never heard her own calf).

South Devon calf with a Beltie coat

As the calf was freshly taken from its own mum and not going to be hungry yet, we shut it in a corner of the handling pen, so the cow could smell it through the hurdle. By the evening, she was delighted when we released 'her baby', which had also miraculously come back to life. Gyp-the-Wonder-Dog looked on, hoping for some cleansings, or possibly some milky calf poop to disgrace himself with – you'll never accept welcoming licks from Gyp-the-Wonder-Dog, if you take my advice. This piqued her protective nature even more. Our only concern was that the blinking calf mightn't go to the cow, knowing he was looking for a big orange mum. Not a bit of it, he went straight in, and she readily let him feed. I don't know if I've ever seen such a definite result, although you'll agree, few have such an attractive colour scheme!

They are out to moor now, looking pretty ridiculous.

While on the aforementioned overnight trip up onto the Wiltshire plains, I noticed that a lot of barley was already in ear, despite being barely clear of the flints. I'm told that it won't grow any taller now, which must mean that, come August, there won't be many calls begging me to take another load of straw. While we haven't had it as dry this spring as last year, and there is still a chance of getting an average shear of grass – I'm only just chucking stock out of the last mowing ground to stand up – the national forage outlook isn't overly bright. We'll see d'rectly.

Of much more interest while up on the chalk, we were sat in a pub one evening, awaiting our sumptuous repast. To while away the time, my beloved and I were reading the local papers. I was greatly taken by an ad for an upcoming festival. The bill featured 'New Model Army', 'The Rezillos', 'The UK Subs' and, curiously, 'The Wurzels'. Strange bedfellows we thought, although I'm almost tempted to go along, just to see 'Peter and the Test Tube Babies' if nothing else.

Alison meanwhile was browsing the results of some produce show. Now we all know that a judge doesn't have to present a first prize, especially if the field isn't, er, very broad. (I had to judge a class of one bull last summer, and had to make a reasonable display of ensuring he was a beast fit to receive the

prize – to make sure I'd earned my dinner in the VIP tent, if nothing else), but here, Alison found one better.

There were several classes in which no first prize had been awarded, suggesting a very poor turnout, or just a hard judge, but in the 'Bottled Vegetable' category he'd seen fit to award nothing more than a third place rosette. Jeez Louise! What had ole Fred squidged into a jar to only qualify for a third? The mind boggles.

Devon County Show

I can report that I had a grand day out Friday last, at the Devon County Show. I spent most of it relaxed in the cattle shed leaning on a new thumb stick – kindly fabricated by our old pal Nick Bibby, in holly, Sherberton bog oak, and curiously, camel bone. I passed the time of day with old friends and new, mostly discussing how little rain we'd all

Dory the show heifer takes a nap

had, or just chewing the fat. Cattle Steward Mr Gilbert (who must surely have had other duties) tickled us mightily with inspirational theories on the niceties of polite behaviour in alternative cultures. While I can hardly repeat them here, I might strongly advise against holidaying with Nick in the Orient.

My boy John had helped Alison Bunning fluff up a couple of Riggit heifers on Thursday, where they acquired a few rosettes. Then I was shanghai-ed into following behind them, as they jockeyed up to take part in the Grand Parade. Those of you who witnessed the ensuing performance will appreciate how long it took to train these heifers to behave just so. Mrs Bunning got halfway up the chute to the ring before bottling it, as her heifer danced about, shoving her around. The boy, being made of stern stuff, determined that he would lead his charge onwards without her sister. As you might have seen, he got halfway round the ring before she took her cue, and jumped up to land on his heel. I smartly took over, so he could hobble along trying to maintain his dignity. By the time we passed the commentator's rostrum 'Dory' was badly in need of some nasal jewellery, or possibly a sedative. Sorry to disappoint – I believe there was a book running on whether we'd complete any of the zigzag arrangement – but I turned right as we completed our first lap. Curiously, I then found myself in a log jam of equally stroppy cattle, also trying to hurriedly exit the ring (must have been something in the air). Dory didn't really want to wait, and tried to tunnel under someone else's beast. Once we'd sorted that out, and I'd got her back in the lines, I dropped her rope as she barged in beside her sister like nothing had happened. Swine. They were generally the most placid dopes you ever saw, with all and sundry coming in to scratch their shaggy heads. When they sat down to cud, our kids would lie on them, for all the world like a litter of puppies or piglets piled up.

Ironically, as the better-behaved cattle returned from their completed parade, a couple of Shorthorn bulls took spectacular and noisy exception to each other, briefly clearing the lines quicker than the four-minute warning.

At least retreating early allowed us to get in first for cream teas, kindly supplied by that nice Mr Harper. He even saw fit to settle our nerves with a

warming draught of what he assured me was 'cold tea'. Cheers Bill.

I hear Dory did Saturday's parade sporting some ironwork in her snout, meek as dishwater. But hey! Where's the fun in that?

Anyway, stockman Joe has decided he and John could rodeo one of our retained heifers off the hill, to enliven future such events. Last seen he was marching up to the moorgate, heading into the fog with a rope halter and a determined look in his eye. Hmm.

John's white heifer

The boy is in a huff this morning. His last black ewe has finally lambed, but had a white lamb, while his precious White Galloway heifer has just borne a black calf. Seeing as this means both lamb and calf must now revert to 'Daddie's hay fund' I suppose he's right to be miffed.

Rosie the White Galloway (see overleaf) *Photograph by David Howard*

The white heifer caused much hilarity as a calf. She is a rare 'red pointed', meaning she has red ears and nose, and was an outstanding and striking calf. She was born to one of my Whites, and I traded her with the boy, for a crossbred cow of his. She'd developed severe behavioural issues and needed to have her head cut off hurriedly. I gave him the pick of my Whites, seeing as the 'Berserker' represented half his herd, and without a moment's thought he asked for the red pointer. Fine choice, we all agreed.

Then, a few months later, a farming pal from 'Oop North' (none other than Tim Wilson, of The Ginger Pig fame*) was visiting and took a fancy to this calf. On the second day of his visit – after first checking with me – he set about trying to buy it. But the boy, who would've been about eight at the time, wouldn't have a bit of it. No figures were discussed, which was probably just as well, as Tim is known to pay serious wedge when something takes his eye. I believe John might have been turning down a couple of grand for this heifer.

Now I do want all of my kids to know how many beans make five, believing that understanding such things is more important to them than almost anything they'll learn in skool. On balance though, I'm glad the boy places a higher value on such things than mere cash.

His concept of values was reaffirmed recently when one of his hides come back from tanning. It's from a deep-red Riggit marked steer, who went down the road with a full winter jacket. This is always a high-risk venture, as the hair can get mashed and mangled, and you can easily end up with a ruined hide. It has, however, come back beautiful, with long soft coat in the most lustrous colour. It's one of the best hides we've seen, and I'd expect to put several hundred quid on its price tag. Is it for sale? Not once junior had seen it, it wasn't. It was whisked away, and he's refusing to discuss the matter.

Oh well.

* *Infamous high-end butcher-cum-Yorkshire farmer and raconteur*

'Organic' farmers

I seem to be developing a habit for absorbing various news articles, and then letting them merge into one amorphous lump of thought, which ends up overlapping in my fog-bound memory. Perhaps it's my age.

This week I've been reading various reports on the Soil Association conference, alongside learned reaction to Sir John what's-his-face's report (Bedlington – or is that a terrier?) on the challenge of feeding a rising world population. In between, I keep feeling I'm missing out by not covering my whole acreage in solar panels, but knowing in my heart that there'll be a major row about the cost of such subsidised electricity. For good measure, I ordered my few tonnes of 20-10-10 fertiliser, and then had to take a seat while Mike went to get the oxygen mask. Meanwhile, Alison mutters darkly about something called the 'Farmed Environment' campaign.

All of these bits of information swirl about as I trundle along between groups of cattle, or spend another boring session square-edging some oak boards. Several conclusions have bubbled to the top of the fermenting froth, although I don't think I'll be able to string them together very neatly for you.

First off, if I hear one more 'organic' or environmental pundit use the term 'sustainable', I'll choke. Anyone – whatever their credentials – using one drop of fossil fuel cannot ever use that label. Pretending to be bunny-hugging and earth-friendly whilst pumping unleaded into your car, or tilling your land with cherry-ade (red diesel to you pal) or, best of all, flying to Mexico to discuss it all, is peddling an untruth. The resource is being used up, and will soon be gone. It follows therefore that its use is unsustainable.

I know and accept this, as I plan to sprinkle some granules on my mowing ground, fully intending to utilise some hydrocarbon bale wrap when I come to cut the grass and the weather closes in on me. I'm not happy about it, but at least I'm not going to make crass claims, or imply some 'holier than thou' high ground.

Sorry. I don't mean to upset anyone… really, the postman struggles with the hate mail as it is. Oh, and as far as I can see, there's three main types of

organic farmers. There's the dyed-in-the-wool diehards, who run their lives by the cycles of the moon, and tend their Hebridean ewes in sandals. Good for them… man. Then there's the conventional farmers, who're lured into organics by the subsidies/premium price outputs. Good for them as well. (Some of them play by the rules, while others, hush my mouth, seem to pay the barest lip service to the Soil Association.) And, to be fair, there are some serious commercial farmers, who genuinely strive to find ways to produce food, in a manner 'more sustainable'. (Good grief, I'm using the damned phrase now.) Them I do respect, although I do wish all the above would stop moralising.

Sorry, back to the foggy route I was meandering along. With concerns about how we'll feed nine billion mouths when the natural gas runs out, or the water available for irrigation dries up, I'm none too sure how it can all be made to stack up. In fact, I'm not sure why nine billion by the year so-and-so is the number to discuss. What happens the year after that? Perhaps Sir Bedlington has looked beyond nine billion, and doesn't like to talk about what he sees.

I don't know about you old pal, but I ken all too well what happens when you – or I – try to keep way too many animals in one place. The logistics become increasingly unfeasible, the health status plummets, and a crash is inevitable. It is a fundamental lesson any stock farmer learns, either the easy way, or the hard. Human beings are little different. The same laws apply. The only discussion is where the crash comes.

We already live in a seven-billion-strong hive, where each element of the whole population is impacting every other part. It gets more complex all the while, with human nature remaining what it is (we all want everything, now). I can't see a pain-free way out, but I can see that all the pieces I've been reading about last week are part of this jigsaw.

(OK then, if you insist. The first fumbling steps forward might include some kind of initiative test to qualify to vote – which will rule me out – and some mechanism to put decision-making in the hands of folk not influenced by a four-to-five-year term in office. You work out the detail, and let me know.)

SUMMER 2011

Shooting camels

I am vaguely involved in a carbon capture/saving project. It is, globally, a relatively small scheme exploring the potential to (a) capture carbon, then (b) store it and (c) quantify how much we're already storing. My place in operations is fairly low level ('token peasant' being my title), and we're still mostly at the 'gathering data' and 'exploring possibilities' stage. The scientists on the team are all very excited about the technical matters arising and saving the world. Meanwhile, I am keeping a weather eye on the possibility in earning real revenue selling carbon credits. You see one of the possible outcomes of the project is that it might just be feasible to persuade some industrial interest, or other wanton consumer of fossil fuels, to pay us to 'maintain' something we've already got.

Joe Public could apparently then go on flitting over to some sub-tropical beach for a week's winter sun, or changing his car every fortnight, without troubling his conscience. This is obviously a manifest nonsense, and not much better than the 'plant a tree' twaddle*, which is supposed to spare us the effects of global warming and climate change. All I can do is try to grab a slice of 'silly cake' while it's still being shared out.

I feel doubly obliged to do so after discovering that, upon changing the wife's car, I was involuntarily persuaded to contribute to one of these insane funds myself. I tried to cry that I was exempt, but apparently I'm not. So it's OK that we've hacked a couple of tonnes of steel/bauxite/plastics from the earth's guts to manufacture this car, because someone somewhere has planted a cherry tree with my name on it.

What is the word? Bullocks.

Remember, this is to offset the carbon you've released burning oil, or coal or natural gas, which was grabbed from the atmosphere over hundreds of thousands of years. As I said, it is a manifest nonsense.

I did have a laugh at one of these schemes last week, however. It may have escaped your attention, but you can now pay into a fund to counter your reckless excesses by sponsoring an Australian, in some remote outback station, to go and shoot a few wild camels. This will stop them burping up ever greater quantities of methane, and single-handedly save the world and salve your conscience.

I like it. I really like it. In fact, never mind camels, if you'd care to just slip a few twenties in my hand, I'll nip out and knock over a Dartmoor pony or two. That'll help, won't it? Better yet, for a little extra, I'll allow you to come and pull the trigger yourself.

I can see it now. With a little imagination and deft marketing, I could sell the stalking rights to some stressed-out industrialist from Dortmund. He could spend a drizzly week up on an under-grazed boulder-strewn ridge, inching slowly closer to a majestic semi-feral stallion, with a view to blowing it to kingdom come, while simultaneously offsetting his factory's plumes of pollution. I suppose we could attach fake antlers if he thinks they'd look better. There will need to be some kind of hunting lodge provided, with a well-stocked bar, and comely chalet maids. I imagine he'll be wearing some traditional tweed/lederhosen combination, and a jaunty hat with a small feather sticking upright in the side.

And if finding his quarry is proving difficult, all Fritz would have to do would be hang around one of the ice-cream vans that park up on moorland lay-bys locally. The targets are much easier there, if the chances of collateral damage are somewhat higher.

Right, I'm off to see if I can get some kind of start-up funding…

*To help you grasp the enormity of this untruth, I'll explain. There is a growing industry that will, if you pay them, plant some trees on your behalf to offset your fossil fuel usage-carbon footprint. The idea being that these trees will absorb carbon dioxide from the atmosphere as they grow, locking it up in wood. What providers tend to gloss over, whilst persuading you to give them money, is that the trees will have a life expectancy of perhaps less than a century. And unless the timber is then preserved very carefully indeed, it will soon rot away, releasing all the carbon it soaked up. To be really generous, some timber might be used in construction, and protected for, say, another century.

Couriers

I want to know how many of us really subscribe to the privatisation concept. Not me, for one. While I'm all for sharpening up procedure and management in public sectors grown distant from reality, there are some things I would rather remained in the hands of the State. The Post Office is one of these.

Lately we've had a couple of 'heads up' warnings that commercial parcel couriers are going to cut us off, on account of being too isolated. First a package containing pins and bushes for the timber crane got lost on its way from Dumfries (Barrie had decided we were going to fix these pins before they 'fixed' themselves). After waiting for a day or two, I phoned the manufacturer – and this is another instance where I'm glad to have bought British, as I don't speak very good Finnish. Mind, I need to concentrate to converse with the tartan natives north of the border. The parts had reappeared at the supplier, having journeyed to Dartmoor and back again. Apparently I wasn't home on any of the numerous occasions the courier had tried to make the delivery.

This was something of an untruth, I explained to my pal 'Ewan'. The yard is staffed pretty much every minute of every day and every night, and it would have been quite a feat for a van to pull up and leave again unnoticed on the occasions claimed. Never mind if he'd bothered to knock on the door, sound his horn, or made any effort whatsoever. No, I'm afraid the courier company was lying.

Then Alison was waiting on a parcel which was a day or two late. When it did arrive, it bore a note explaining that it had been delayed because we had supplied an 'insufficient address'. Funnily enough, the details we supplied were the proscribed ones the Post Office uses, including the postcode. I thought everyone used these fangled satnavs now – except me, admittedly, I use a thing called a map – which could've brought the presumptive Stanley to Dr Livingstone by teatime, using the shortest and least crocodile-infested route possible. Another lie?

Now if I were a big cheese in a courier firm, I would have a bespectacled geek crunching delivery times and routes through a gurt big computer to discover how to trim the fat any way I could. It's a highly competitive market, and one of the areas that would raise my financial hackles would be 'out of the way' drops to addresses out in the sticks.

Whether the effects I'm witnessing are just sporadic incompetence, or the thin end of a pending wedge, remains to be seen. But these companies are the ones who will want to take over if the Post Office should go.

Another aspect of living near the edge of civilisation are telecommunication problems (privatisation issues arise here as well). We do have a broadband connection (although it isn't very broad), and whatever Cuddly Dave promised, we suffer regular interruption. I accept this, as BT has to maintain a long tangly strand of copper wire to get to us. When it breaks, we have to wait for a day or two, and try not to blub about it.

But when service was down again lately one of the kids got in a real tiz. It seems the internet was required to complete vital homework for school. I have taken exception to this before… what about households without a computer? But I'm firmly put in my place by people who imagine every home has the required gear, and a reliable connection. Apparently kids with such inadequate family support can use skool computers during break time. What, and wear 'Backward Impoverished Hick' placards around their little necks while doing so?

My contempt for professionals allowing rural kids to become further marginalised in this way is huge. Really huge. I'm not much enamoured of the idea of further privatising the Telecom network either.

Sorry. I'll calm down again.

Baling – and restless bulls

Like some of you, I've taken advantage of some better weather, and made a start on the hay last week. We've started with some off ground, unstocked since the winter. The mower gets around about 47 acres, most of it in sensible-sized fields, with only moderate slopes to work on. We'll venture into more testing territory later.

The ground is in a pretty dry parish, and couldn't be described as 'heavy land' without a severe 'Pinocchio nose' incident. And sure enough the dry spring hasn't helped yield, with the shear being pretty light along the thinner slopes.

Belted Galloways in the Swincombe Valley

Perversely, where the cows had loafed about last winter, away from the round feeders, and pooped, there was a reasonable cut, which took a bit of drying. The whole job became a game of two halves. The thinner patches were ready to bale almost before they were turned out, but then fell to chaff as soon as the baler got near, while daily stirring about wasn't making much headway in the thicker spots. The chaffy stuff has been a nightmare to bale, falling between the belts and lodging in every crevice it can find. As you track along the contour, it spills down the pick-up reel, and dribbles out the side (I dribble out the side when I'm tired and emotional mind). Of course, baling uphill works fine, but then you have to come back down again, and that works not at all. Harrumph.

Several bales fell to bits at various stages, no matter how much string I put on them, and when the baler finally got completely clogged up there was no alternative but for yours truly to immerse himself and pull it all out again. After 10 minutes in that hellhole I was sneezing handfuls of

the stuff, and my arms and torso were coated in dust and chaff. For good measure, the clouds of floating 'fines' were clogging the tractor's radiator mesh, causing some local difficulties there as well. With alarm klaxons sounding, the clogged mesh couldn't be accessed due to a stuck bonnet catch. I fretted for a bit, before discovering I could knock the built-up crud off by slapping the bonnet really hard. That certainly felt good.

Further excitement was met when a shear bolt went pop, and a search revealed a spare to be 15 miles away. (I'd carefully emptied my pockets before chucking yesterday's diesel- and dirt-encrusted clothes in the wash, but had failed to recharge the clean trouser pockets with the selection of useful knick-knacks.) Luckily, a bolt was quickly scavenged from elsewhere, and a piece of cord securing the part relieved of its bolt, but not before I was covered afresh in dust.

For two pins, I'd try baling the damned stuff with the dew on it (the Aussies often have to do that, as it goes).

Anyway, I finally got clear of the horrid rubbish, and into some better grass. This went through the baler a dream, although most of it would've benefited from another day, which the Met Office say I ain't going to get.

At the time of writing – for there is a satellite delay between us – there are still about 200 round bales to pack away, and only one day to bale 'em in. Fingers crossed.

Back on the ranch, the bulls are all getting restless. The top Beltie has decided his cows ought to calve a bit earlier, having spotted a bunch of them within just one modest bit of steeplechasing. I'm looking the other way for a couple of days. The red Riggit and the Angus are scrapping something awful, knowing that their harems will soon be sorted out for them – if the old Belt hasn't got there first. Meanwhile a homebred yearling, who has been retained to do a specific odd job before his head comes off, has been dropped with a little bunch of cows. While being handled, he kicked me for my troubles. If I'd known he was going to do

that, I'd have knocked the little beggar's head off without permitting him his bit of fun. Ungrateful wretch.

Egbert and the plastic pipe

Tonight, with the dust still clinging to my extremities, I knocked off round baling as the dew fell. It was one of those long days in the tractor, taking in both ends of the scale. Midday found me on the level-est field at home, a long narrow 13 acres, packing away some lovely leafy stuff, which would need wrapping. I could leave the 'B crew' dealing with these, when I went onto my next task. The field is a dream to bale, with rows stretched out into the distance and absolutely no thought to where I could pitch out the bales (we'd done the headlands and short work last week). The only impediment to my life was that it was a fairly thick shear, and I had to watch I didn't stuff too much into the baler's throat at once.

Then, mid-afternoon, I set sail for a collection of two- to three-acre fields a few miles down the road. Joe had turned it a couple of times, and reckoned it was coming fit. I'd sent an operative on ahead to fluff it around until I arrived, whereupon he went rowing up, and I chased him with the baler. An overcast sky, and no guarantee of a dry night focussed my mind, as I charged up and down these little fields in a very respectable crop of hay. But as the work got further down over the hill, in ever smaller fields, so the long day started to tell. The last field to be baled yielded about 15 bales, and every damned one of them had to be carefully placed away from the danger zone. The ground hangs out over a steep combe, below which a number of cottages nestle. Back gardens lie right under the slope, 200 feet below, complete with kiddies' slides and paddling pools and such.

Those of you who've lived this life will know what was on the cards, and so did I. When one went, I saw it go, and chased it down with the baler tractor before it could pick up enough speed to get away, but it was a near-run thing. What I wasn't expecting was when my helpful assistant (rowing up with the loader tractor) moved one which was in the way and placed it against the hedge, and that beggar went as well. It hit the stock fence across

the slope as fast as I could've run, bounced vertically in the air above head height, and dropped back to stop against the wire. Phew.

Egbert, meanwhile, has had an equally near miss – only with an officer of the state. See, there is this fresh-faced, cleanly scrubbed inspector at the local mart, who stands about ensuring the local peasantry adhere to the many rules and regulations.

Now our friend Egbert had arrived at the mart, for to sell a few stores, and have a catch up with his cronies. The steers had been numbered, and penned, and old Egbert was following their course to see where they were held. Perchance, he might find some unsuspecting buyer eyeing them with a view to bidding. Obviously, such a man would need assuring that these fine beasts were exactly what a discerning finisher would be wanting, having had 'one careful owner, and never been raced or rallyed'.

What Egbert actually found was the fresh-faced young official, who upbraided our hero, demanding that he cease carrying the vicious offensive weapon that Egbert often sports (to whit, a cut-off length of old black half-inch plastic water pipe). It seemed that the market now comes under some new set of rules, and that the carrying of such inhumane weapons of torture is now banned.

Egbert was a bit taken aback, having been using such a device for several decades on the premises – certainly since before the inspector was whelped. It especially struck him as ironic, given that old Egbert generally presents unusually docile cattle, which rarely feel the stick. While this mightn't square with his grumpy persona, or the wild unkempt appearance of both cattle and owner, he does concede he's getting no younger, and life is so much easier if the blessed things don't get worked up. Certainly his store cattle generally loaf around the ring, with Egbert scratching their tails as he beseeches the auctioneer to find another bid. The stick usually only comes out to make 'em move on a bit.

So why, he asked, was a piece of bendy plastic so evil? Well, apparently, it is very whippy, and could be used to hurt the cattle. As this discussion was taking place, time-served old drover 'Ron' ambled past. Now Ron

was clutching his accustomed hazel stick. Egbert pointed to this, asking if the hazel was acceptable? Apparently it was.

This rather perplexed Egbert, because while you can't actually do much harm to a beast – or a Government employee come to that – with a piece of alkathene, his old pal Ron's seasoned piece of hazel is about an inch and a quarter through. Given that he's a solid-built old chap, Ron could, if the mood took him, very likely swing it hard enough to… well, to stop dead pretty much anything that was coming at him.

Knowing he was wasting his time pointing this out to the pen pusher, he merely declared that the plastic pipe was in fact a cultural artefact and, barging past the nice young inspector, continued on his way claiming that depriving him would be infringing his human rights.

I later heard that Egbert was a little below par (you may read 'massively hung-over') that morning, having been out on a highly cultural beano the night before (so much so that Mrs Egbert had to drive the Landrover to market). We suspect the lad in the shiny overalls and new boots enjoyed a very lucky escape, narrowly missing the opportunity to find out what can actually be done with a plastic pipe.

A bull in the river

When Joe found Firethorn the Riggit bull absent last week, he did a quick reconnoitre in the Landrover but couldn't find the missing bovine, or a gate open. Seeing as we were busily engaged wrapping some silage at the time we couldn't put much labour to the search right then – for no matter how much grief the cattle give you in the summer, it will be nothing to the trouble they'll give if the cupboard is bare come Christmas.

That night Alison got on her neddy, and clip-clopped out over the obvious territory to search, but to no avail. So, the following afternoon – Saturday – the two of us took a romantic if bouncy trip in the truck, searching increasingly wide areas, phoning the relevant neighbours with the embarrassing news that we were short of a bull. Eventually, he was spied across the Dart, on another property altogether, laying claim to

The author with bull in river (different bull, different assistant!) *Photograph by Ruth Lee*

some Welsh Blacks. How he came to be two enclosures away, with all the gates closed between, remains a mystery. The fences all seem undamaged, and I'm pretty damn sure he didn't fly.

Alison and I drove down to our side of the river, and hopped across the stepping-stones with both carrot and stick (or rather a few kilos of cow cake in a bag, and a couple actual sticks). With very little fuss, we drove him away from his new friends, and down to the river. It was here that things got a bit testy. You see, he didn't bother using the ford, right beside the stones, but rather waded in 50 feet downstream, taking a shortcut. (He was beginning to bellow, knowing he was approaching the realm of his nemesis, Peter the Angus.) Throwing pebbles at his rump, I persuaded him to get across the river, but he baulked at the far bank – it was a bit of a clamber up over just there. I did tell him he should've used the crossing place just upstream, but he merely stood at bay, up to his chest in the river, alternately fertilising the fish and roaring his magnificence.

So, as my beloved went across the stepping-stones to open the gate in readiness, I had little option but to wade in after the cussed beast, and explain the error of his ways. This was not what I really wanted in my life, but hey-ho, he was soon up and out, and marching back up the opposite hill to his rightful realm. (The Angus stayed out of sight, trumpeting how brave he was from a safe distance.)

Buoyed by our success, I recalled we'd earlier noted a Scotch ram sulking behind a rock, looking bothered. Obviously, in high summer, this could mean invertebrate passengers, so we diverted to check him out. Sneaking up – still squelching – behind the rock I leapt on him, catching him completely by surprise. But rather than being at death's door, and needing immediate attention, he was in fact snoozing peacefully, and was none too pleased to be woken in such a manner. After wrestling him manfully to the ground (read, being dragged 20 feet) I ascertained that he was as clean as a whistle, and let him go again.

When we finally got home, thinking we'd tidied up the loose ends for another day, we discovered the kids had gone for a walk with Joe, and lost the boy's blinking Jack Russell down a hole. Great, just great. Another peaceful day in our sleepy bucolic lives.

Chatting with the Riggit bull Firethorn (centre – and who is answering back!) about his wanderings... *Photograph by Alison Bunning*

AUTUMN 2011

Private vs public sector jobs

Having spent a few days with my feet up – on me hols – I've had the chance to read the London papers. I tend to take the *Telegraph* while I'm on the annual jolly, although this is only because it's too much of a fag to arrange the *Western Morning News* from afar.

One of the things that caught my attention is that public sector pay increases are still rolling in automatically, despite a general financial malaise affecting pretty much everything else in the universe. While there's reductions expected in both staff numbers and overall budgets in most state sectors, some of the remaining employees (and surprisingly not always those at the bottom of the heap) are enjoying automatic increased rates of remuneration. That must stick in the craw of those that have been booted out just as much as it does with me.

And before you reach for the poison messenger pigeon, hear about a pal of mine. He does a demanding physical job out in the sticks, and has done so for some decades. Now his job is not only physically tough, but requires a great deal of skill and dexterity. Many are the men I've seen who've failed to make enough money working at the job, and I can count the number of lasses who can earn a living at the particular task on one hand.*

My pal has been self-employed most of his career, and has lived reasonably. His skill level is such that he often wins prizes at international level in his profession – for there is a vibrant and well-sponsored international competition circuit. He has, more than once, been a world champion in these hotly fought international competitions. But, as the years have gone on, he has made a nasty discovery. Like many men before him, he has found that, in the private sector, he is in a world where 'piecework' is the norm, and self-employment means no sick pay or holiday pay, or time off for feeling a bit under the weather.

Being time served does not mean his pay goes up each year, but rather the reverse; as he starts to creak with impending middle age, he cannot deliver as much as he once could. And so his pay goes down.

This is a far cry from one or two of his immediate peers, who found and maintained employment within the state sector. They are now looking at built-up pensions, which keep on maturing with each automatic pay increase. And now, should the rug be pulled out from beneath them, the resultant settlement will mean they can take the pension pretty much straight away.

Obviously, you'll tell me my pal might've built up a healthy reserve when he was going well – and indeed this might very well be the case, for he isn't a clot or a p*sshead. And I am all too aware of the need to ensure that the state jobs pay enough to secure those who work within the machine, but... I am very uncomfortable with the way it has started to look.

Honest and skilled graft in the private sector of rural life often requires extremely careful management of your own affairs to ensure you ever get the chance to stop work. This is not the case in some public sector jobs I can think of, where you've only to keep your head down long enough to rack up the air miles, and you need never worry again.

And I'm so sorry to reveal that naked reality: that there are tasks out in the big bad world, involving physical graft paid on piecework, where most lasses simply cannot 'cut as much cotton' as most fellas, and hence earn less.

A faint shadow of this shocking truth has also been much in the press of late, with great fuss about wimmen not earning as much as blokes in the work place. Apparently some wimmen take time off their work to bear and raise kids, which then leaves them short on 'time served' and missing out on opportunities. Heaven forbid, some employers might even weigh the 'child-bearing age' issue an impediment when considering taking on a young lady. This is of course a huge crime under some law or other. (A pal of mine in Oz knew all about such laws – for they are thick on the ground out there as well. He quietly admitted he exclusively employed older married women, who had raised kids and gone back to work, as his van drivers. They were mostly, he pointed out, sober and wanting to work. But most of all wouldn't need to take maternity leave.)

Anyway, I don't understand any of this. If you try to tip the table to somehow make an allowance for the biologically obvious, surely that becomes equally as discriminating to geezers?

I would have thought satisfactory the traditional arrangement some couples enter. This is the radical idea where one chap and one lass choose to start a family – or at least, realise they have done so inadvertently – and he goes on working to support his wife/partner and their offspring, while she does what nature has equipped her to do. If he can't or won't bring home the bacon, then I'm afraid she made a pretty big mistake.

In our socially just world, even girls who make such mistakes – and their sprogs – are seldom allowed to starve. As far as I am concerned, the more you mess with the obvious natural order of the 'traditional' arrangement – which is the norm throughout cultures across the world, give or take a bit of polygamy – the more you risk fouling things up.

Again, please spare me the hate mail. It must be reading the *Telegraph* for a week that's somehow turned my head.

Digesting silage

To save you the bother, I've been reading up on green energy generation. And, you ought to know, in some cases it is a jolly good idea. In fact, I'm generally all for it. I can see how running a bit of water down a pipe and whizzing up a turbine might make for some pretty guilt-free 'lectric, so long as you leave enough water in the stream for the fish to play about in. I am prepared to accept that a few solar panels on your roof could be a good thing, providing the manufacturing of these panels is defensible (I admit I have no idea if this is the case, or whether your roof is up to the job).

I'd say it was OK to harness the energy from a gusty day on the hilltop, with one of those windfarms which so upset people. (Apparently they ruin the view, although how a nuclear power station you can't see is any more desirable I don't know. I'd have thought that poisonous residue that hangs about for 50,000 years would be pretty ugly however well it's hidden.) And by all means, use the turn of the tides down in the estuary. Fantastic. Get right on with it chaps.

But one of the things I'm not too sure about is something called 'anaerobic digestion'. This seems to involve bubbling vats of organic matter, producing gas which is then burnt in a generator, creating leccy. Well. OK. I can see the potential in this, as long as you stick to some basic parameters. Waste products, cooked up in such plants near to source make sense. Generating a bit of power from the sewage works for instance? Great.

Sadly, approval is also being given to some of these plants to use virgin fuel, ie crops grown specifically for that purpose. Several are planned to swallow, or are already using, silage (maize silage even) to make power for the grid. Smelling a great big green rat, and being a bit of a hick, I got to thinking about this. See, growing and harvesting silage takes fossil fuel. And if you're going to fertilise these crops, lots of it. Some fag packet calculations, a couple of phone calls, and a bit of web research turned up some interesting stuff.

See, making a tonne of ammonia fertiliser takes about 33,500 cubic feet of natural gas. In calorific value, this equals something like 800 litres of crude oil. Of course, there are many variables. For a start you don't use a tonne of ammonia in a tonne of fert, and you might very well be running your forager on used chip oil from the Red Mullet for all I know, but… and here's the awkward bit. The much celebrated fag packet maths (and not being a smoker, this leads to a certain amount of difficulty in itself) suggests that you wouldn't be very much worse off, tonne for tonne, simply burning the blinking fossil fuels in the generator to start with.* That would even leave you with a few acres spare over which you might want to, say, run a few ewes.

Heaven forbid, if we're talking about maize silage, the implication is that you're doing all this on ploughable land, in a reasonably favoured spot. Jeepers, isn't that then directly traceable to someone going hungry, just so we can turn on the telly/run the dishwasher?

I should say – before any of the interested parties reach for an injunction, or the old over-and-under – that I don't care very much one way or another. If the feed-in-tariff makes it profitable – which is obviously the only way such nonsense can achieve lift off – go right ahead old pal. In fact, by spending massive sums on infrastructure that ties up your land for years, you'll only help drive up the price of food.

Like so many of these fantastic plans, the economics stand on the thinnest of ice. The projected scheme above relies on silage being valued at £30/tonne – it doesn't say how soggy the tonne was. This figure will become a very movable feast, as input costs go up, and will be held against a rising market price for beef anyway.

It parallels some Clever Dicks famously putting in various wood-fuelled systems in recent years, because pulpwood was languishing around £20/tonne roadside (this price barely covering the felling and extraction, which in itself should've rung the old alarm bells). Why on earth would woodland owners and managers replant and invest at that rate? The answer of course is that foresters guessed that trade would pick up d'rectly. And sure enough, roadside timber prices have moved dramatically in the last couple of years. But for the advanced felling of masses of infected larch flooding the market, I suspect there would already be several red faces.

And do please stop shouting at this page. I've got my fingers in my ears, and I'm singing 'La la la la'.

Some more numbers, for those of you still paying attention. A projected plant on a hypothetical 300-acre farm is said to be likely to annually produce 1,216,000kWh. This is equal to 4,377,600MJ of energy according to a clever calculator I found, or 97 tonnes of crude. A call to a pal who generates a bit of leccy from a diesel gen-set suggests he'd make almost double that kWh from that kind of volume of fuel (depending on the conversion of crude to diesel). I got distracted then, and stopped my research there; I couldn't make sense of the wheeze, however I tried.

And by the by, how much bio-diesel, for instance, could you grow on 300 acres?

Slowcoach

Quite apart from creaking and groaning after spending an intense week chasing rows of grass – another 300 bales, happily including some that won't need wrapping – I am not an especially jovial bunny just now.

Some of you will know that I finally allowed stockman Joe to halter-break a Riggit heifer, which he then led round the ring at the Bath & West this last June. I've never held much with showing cattle off Coaker Hall, on the grounds that we're always going to be on the back foot against pretty much anyone else. What with the inclement climate and thin ground, coupled with my spectacular thrift with the cake bag and my widely acknowledged general incompetence, the trophy cabinet is hardly likely to be overburdened.

Nonetheless, as well as helping to showcase some Riggit stock, we all agreed that it might be fun. And so it was. Even Slowcoach the heifer enjoyed it; like her sisters (that Mrs Bunning shows) she is an amiable soul, equally happy out on the veldt or being pawed by the masses.

Now while this was going on, I had rather scurrilously negotiated the sale of this heifer – unbeknown to poor Joe – and as soon as she came back from her outing, she had to be 'pre-movement' TB tested. Unfortunately she was an 'Inconclusive Reading'. This isn't the end of the world; we've had occasional IRs before, and they've always come clean on the 60-day retest.

Well not this time old bean. Because she was a retest, she had a pretty severe set of callipers applied next time round, and although the readings were down – they probably wouldn't have raised any attention at all normally – she is now a double IR, which makes her a 'Reactor'. We have now lost our 'TB free' status. (With the dazzling efficiency of the State Veterinary Service*, three weeks after her retest we still hadn't been told what her second IR meant, and I had to ring and ask.) I think it extremely unlikely that she's got TB. Our main herd test earlier in the spring was as clean as a whistle. (This in itself raises some tricky questions, which I've no interest in asking, but someone ought.)

Anyway, my phoning on Tuesday last revealed Slowcoach is going for slaughter this Wednesday. I did probe what were to happen if a rambler should leave a gate open, and she should be lost out to moor? (As I've mentioned, this is a daily issue for me all through the summer.) Not surprisingly, I was soon told that it would be a cross-compliance matter, and that my Single Farm Payment would be jeopardised. Being a poor-ass tenant farmer, and reliant on the payments, this effectively means I stand to lose my family home if I don't lower my gaze.

I am now rueing my reluctant admission into the one club I didn't really ever wish to join. (I say, is there a bar? I really could do with a drink.) *Those of you who've known me a bit longer will recall I've had extremely difficult relations with the SVS since 2001. And now it seems they want to start again and, frankly, it's pretty hard to keep my composure.*

Burst pipe

Living and farming in rainy peat-clad hills, it's inevitable that I encounter the Water Board, or whatever they're called now. Sorry, if that sounds a bit vague, but do bear in mind that on land I'm farming there are water catchments, dams and weirs established by three different borough councils. There's various stone and concrete markers set on boundaries to this effect, dating from long before 'South West Water'. Water mains and leats run hither and thither around the moors, distributing aqua vita to distant urban centres.

Now a few weeks back, I was looking in on a little bunch of off-lying cattle of a Sunday, and noticed smoke rising half a mile further down the valley. 'Oh,' I said to myself, 'I've got campers down in the woods', resolving to go and have a little chat with them later, possibly tapping them for enough cash to fill my flagon with foaming ale at The Strangled Ferret. I forget what then distracted me – something of great excitement no doubt – but they went right out of my mind.

Then, Tuesday morning, I was carrying half a bag of sweeties up to some steers lying far above this valley, and blow me if there wasn't still smoke rising. Mind, whoever it was they must have been struggling to keep a little campfire alight, as it was a bit drizzly, and the smoke was pretty white and steamy. Anyway, 'We won't be having this' I told Gyp. (Gyp-the-Wonder-Dog cannot sit in the back of the truck while I go up and see these steers, but has to sneak after me, hiding in the gorse until I see him.) We headed off down in the direction of this smoke, and soon realised that it was in fact the top of a huge fountain of water, rising right from where a 24-inch main runs down the valley. This main bottoms out just about at this point before it begins to climb out over the next hill towards its goal, making this the point of highest pressure, and the fountain sure was a beaut.

Hopping in the truck, I headed home to make the call. Sadly, due to ever-tightening funds, the authority concerned no longer lists phone numbers for individual works, or even keeps them manned at all times. As it goes, I still had the number for the local works, but couldn't get anyone to pick up the receiver.

Right, said I, I'll ring the main number listed for leaks. This put me through, eventually, to an operator in some distant office – he did have an English accent, but I have no idea where he was actually sat. We had a difficult conversation, as he ran down his checklist of what to say. I suppose the 'Helpline' tackles all manner of matters, leaks being just one, and he couldn't help having the IQ of a teabag. When we finally managed to concur that I was reporting a leak, he needed to know what the postcode was. 'There ain't one son, it's half a mile from the nearest property the postie can get to.' A blank silence followed. 'Well what would be the nearest postcode?' Given this, and the name of the two reservoirs at either end of this 24-inch main – and I'm pretty sure the Water Authority would retain a working map of where they leave reservoirs and 24-inch mains – he asked if this would place the leak 'near Mevagissey?' ('Out by about 70 miles, son'). We eventually agreed that he'd get someone to phone me back and ask for more info. I rather hoped that this would be someone who could manage complex tasks, like walking upright or counting to 10.

Some little while later, I found myself on the phone to another operative. This one could very well have been a first cousin to the first, as we went through it all again. This time, I was ahead of him, and gave him a grid reference, although his grasp of this led me to conclude that cousins get no further than first in this particular tribe. I tried suggesting he simply phoned the big depot at such and such – which certainly is manned – and tell whoever answered the phone that Anton Coaker had seen a gurt leak on the main between X and Y. 'No no, that's not how the system works,' he assured me, still grasping at where the leak might be. 'Well give me the soddin' number, I'll phone them meself.' No, he couldn't do that – and anyway, how was I sure it was a pipe leaking? 'Well, Maister, I'd a' thought the 40-foot fountain would be the giveaway.' I lost interest by this point, and left it with him so I get on with my own work.

A few hours later, I was headed off on some mission or other, and noted as I passed that the vapour was still boiling down in the valley, but no white vans were parked up where they might be. Oh well, I thought, I did try. Then, further down the road I did meet one of the vans, driven by an old lad who tends local works. I tried flagging him down, but he didn't notice, so I turned round in pursuit. Timing it to the yard, I came up behind him, and persuaded him to pull over. Getting out to meet me, I led the amiable old chap over to the hedgebank, pointed him down into the deep valley in the direction of the geyser, and asked if this would be of any interest. I can't repeat what he exclaimed when he saw our water feature, nor would I wish to perform the task requested. He then went on to observe that this might be why he'd noticed a drop in pressure further down.

And no, he hadn't been sent by head office, he was merely trundling out to check the intake works.

So now a team has arrived, with a couple of swingers* and some new pipe, but I'm wondering. Is there a keen young engineer, sent from head office, still down in the depths of Cornwall, jobsheet in hand and looking for a fountain?

* 360-degree excavator, short for swing shovel (not the other type of swingers...)

Solar panels

Following on from some unfortunate comments I might've made somewhere, about the highly dubious numbers purveyed by the vendors of various alternative energy systems, I'll put the other foot in it.

I strongly suspect that some schemes are in fact 'the Emperor's new sustainable clothes'. Not, you understand, that I'm against the concept per se. It is abundantly clear that fossil fuels are going to rocket in price, and do you really want to rely on Mr Putin's generosity to be able to turn up the heating in years to come? Or would you rather bequeath the opportunity for your great grandchildren to deal with the glow-in-the-dark waste from messing around with nuclear power?

We simply have to start down the road of making our power from renewable sources, and the sooner we get on with it, the less of a shock it will be. But some current plans look suspiciously like they're nonsense.

While out and about in the truck last week, heading east, I passed the first large-scale solar panel set-up I've seen in a field. Lads were fixing these things up in great rows, right beside the road. And what upset me? Why, the lads in fluorescent jackets were covering a field of beautifully tillable ground. I haven't checked the map, but if this arable ground wasn't grade one, it was pretty darn good. It was a level, well-drained sandy tilth, straight out of cropping, and being covered up.

Meanwhile all along the verge of the trunk road other teams in hi-vis coats were using various machines to mow the weeds and trash growing up and down the roadside embankments. The same day, I passed redundant roadside chew-and-spew cafés, acres of industrial unit roof space, poor scrub ground, and all manner of places where solar panels could be put with little or no net loss. What an absurd situation. Someone needs their backside kicking in the biggest possible manner.

Returning home, a snippet in the timber press caught my attention. A worthy industrial-scale consumer of wood has raised the point that a trio of proposed new UK bio-mass plants could consume the entire annual UK wood crop. While I'm not sure he can be right – although the figures are readily available, and he is a man in a position to know – it did remind me of something.

I recall crunching some numbers backalong, when some bright spark at Westminster realised that you can, unbelievably, burn sticks to heat your house. Even better, he'd discovered nature then regrows more sticks for you. Hey, these universities don't half turn out some geniuses! This groundbreaking news prompted me to have a stab at working out how many sticks 70 million people might burn, and the answer quickly scaled up to mean about half of the UK land surface would have to be afforested (and be in careful management at that) to do the trick. Sorry Einstein, it's back to the drawing board for you.

And now another thing occurs. After looking at all the complicated hi-tech renewable schemes (the workings of which baffle poor old peasants like me), I had a brainwave.

See, you can buy a big diesel generator for a fairly modest sum, and I'm led to believe that it isn't rocket science to run such a device on bio-diesel (vegetable oil with the sugars distilled out of it, in short). This stuff might cost a bit more than red diesel, but hey, if you're kicking out 100–200 KVA, and can swear blind that it is renewable, won't the 'Feed-in-tariff' make it all a jolly nice little earner? Get the supply contract, organise the fuel supply, buy the genny, fire her up and watch the cash roll in… simple. (We'll neatly forget to factor in the conventional diesel used to grow the veg oil initially. I don't think anyone is asking very searching questions in the rush anyway.)

Look, I'm a bit busy just now, but if this is a runner you will buy me a pint, won't you?

Right, I've got to slip off to a bull sale. I don't need a bull, but I see that 'a vet will inspect each bull between 8 and 8.30am'. Seeing as there are 22 bulls entered he's got rather less than 90 seconds per beast, and I'm not wanting to miss seeing such a man at work.

List of injuries

I was bemoaning recently my needing medical attention. (A trapped nerve was just about setting my arm ablaze.) This got me thinking about the times I have had the quack prod me about.

Apart from youthful slides down the tarmac beside/under a motorbike, resulting in various nurses spending many happy hours picking bits of 10mm grit out of my knees/elbows, and applying that fizzing peroxide stuff, I've been to the doctor/A&E for (in no particular order):

- **Ringworm**
- **Orf** (luckily quickly diagnosed by doc who kept a few ewes)
- **Farmer's lung** (that was a 'go directly to hospital, do not pass "Go", do not collect £200' job)
- **Tennis elbow** (nailing roof sheets on the baler shed)
- **Squashed big toe** (while clearing windblown trees, much as you might squash an overripe tomato)
- **Bad back** (strangely, right after lifting 300 newly lambed Cheviot ewes into the back of the Landrover over the course of three weeks)
- **Grinding sparks/sawdust/hayseed in the eyes** (professional attention several times)
- **Peeled back flap of flesh from a shin** (from slipping against a nasty piece of angle iron: both required a spot of welding).

You might be spotting a pattern here, in that they're all 'work related'. Lesser medical matters, dealt with at home (or if we're being absolutely candid here, not dealt with at all) are also, without exception, occupational injuries, and have included:

- Various other episodes of **back problems** associated with lifting heavy beams/struggling livestock (shearing the ewe lambs nearly cooked me one year).
- Many variations of **grit/sawdust/hayseed in eyes** extracted at home. (Swivel eyes left to right, first open one way, then close the other. Repeat in reverse, apply eye drops, try leaving overnight and hope the ophthalmic night goblins can sort it out.)
- Numerous **blackened nails.** In fact, I'm usually free of a black nail, although some never seem to achieve a full set. Farmer X (retired) is a top performer in the club, rarely having a full set unblemished. (Well, never nowadays, since the naughty bale elevator nipped the end of a digit off.) I did two nails at once when I was a lad – I put my hand in front of a ewe that turned and bolted in an alleyway. She ran into an RSJ, with my fingers on her forehead. That took my mind of things for a while.

Retrieving a Beltie calf from the river *Photograph by Agnes Coaker*

• **Slicing off the very tip of my finger** in another demonstrably hazardous piece of machinery (luckily it grew back like a lizard's tail).

• **Falling from top of loaded bale trailer** left me with a startlingly vivid imprint of the drawbar stamped across my lower back (don't think I've ever had a closer shave, and spent a few minutes on the ground testing

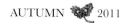

which bits I could still move; happily, the drawbar was a large section bit of steel, with no jack protruding).

• Then there's the usual selection of scars from **gashes and gouges** attained during everyday life wrestling large animals/bits of timber/plant and machinery, often while clutching sharp tools.

• Equally normal has been the assortment of **burns,** from dehorning irons/welding splatter and the like. (Always a favourite is the lump of welding splatter dropping down a boot. That makes you dance. Although the most disturbing was a gob of red-hot splatter finding its way into an earhole, where I could hear the damn thing sizzling its way through me. Mmm. Nice.)

• There have been several fractured **fingers and toes** over the years, which had by turns lost arguments with grumpy cattle, thrashing Dartmoor ponies, runaway round bales and immobile lumps of steel. Fingers you can strap to their chums with insulating tape, toes you just have to avoid stubbing for a few weeks. (NB When you've bust a finger on your right hand, watch out for enthusiastic greetings from show-offs.)

Topping this rogues' gallery of 'auto-first-aid' injuries is something that happened during a catchy harvest backalong.

While hard-pressed round baling in front of the building storm clouds, a blockage had me pulling lumps of wedged haylage free of the baler's pick-up reel (which was turned off at the time, I might add). Desperate to get on, I pulled too hard and whipped an arm down onto the pick-up tines. These were sharpened to a fine edge from years of brushing the crop off the floor, and one stuck right into my wrist. Yelping, I pulled it away, to reveal a neat 5mm puncture hole. This immediately began welling up, pushing out however much blood was pumping down that particular bit of my plumbing in a distinctly alarming fashion. It was just about squirting out the hole like a fountain. Not wanting to lose the sun, I wrapped my handkerchief around it fairly tight, and discovered that, if I bent my hand backwards, this makeshift bandage pulled tight enough to stop the flow (if it did make the hand go a bit white). Obviously, the various actions required during the bale-making cycle necessitated releasing this pressure, which I surmised would probably allow a bit of circulation to stave off gangrene or anything like that. By the time the clouds gathered the hole seemed to have stopped leaking, even if it had gone a tiny bit blue. And I'd got a couple hundred more bales packed up. Result!

I daresay, as age and infirmity catches up with me, there'll be inevitable 'worn-out' issues for the doc to look into, but meanwhile, even though the list looks long… by golly I've been lucky.

Hisley Saturn, prior to the unkindest cut of all

WINTER 2011/2012

Daisy

Home on the range the mild November has evaporated, leaving a raw blasted start to December.

This was brought sharply to my attention on Sunday morning when Daisy was missing. Daisy is a very sweet-natured Angus cross cow, reared (and much loved) tied to a stake in a garden, before coming to live here with all her hairy friends. Last winter, Daisy was indoors with an autumn-born Angus calf at foot, and loved the South Devon bull she was lodging with very much. Although she carries a lot of gut ordinarily, she was the size of a whale this year. Still, having five or six calves under her belt, and the South Devon bull being very easy calving, I was quietly confident. I had made sure Joe and I had worked her back through various outlying groups, so she was close to home as she bagged up.

Then, come Sunday morning, she was conspicuous in her absence. After hunting round the two fields where she should have been, I found her two fields further out, having somehow got under/over the fence, to get herself tucked almost down at the bottom of the valley. Unfortunately, it would've been about 3am when I'd needed to have been there, as she was by now cast, upside down (all four legs in the air), with a big calf stuck toes and nose out – and those wedged tight against the drystone wall to boot. As I approached, she waved her legs at me a bit, to show me she was still alive… 'Hello Daddy, wondered when you were going to show up.'

First off, I checked the state of the calf, but it was too late. Its tongue was swollen, and cold, and its eyes had no blink reflex showing. Still, Daisy looked quite chipper, considering her undignified position. I guessed the calf would come away easily enough if I could but get her turned away from the blessed wall a bit. That meant I needn't rush off for the calving aid – it was a long walk back up to the Landrover, never mind going back for gear. And bringing the handler down this far to pull her round is by no means a foregone conclusion once the ground is wet – and it was sodden. And quite apart from all that, being on my tod feeding Sundays, I don't have too many spare minutes to dick around in the shortening daylight.

Right, manpower. Dragging her round to get enough access to baby was a struggle, but we got there. Then, my wet cold hands couldn't grab his toes tightly enough to get him moving. At least Daisy was still game to push a bit, meaning we weren't too late for her. Luckily, a piece of quadrant bale cord was looped over the wall nearby, from when Joe had fastened a hurdle in a gap to detain an errant bull. This might cut into your hands when serving as a calving rope, but not half as much as little bale cord (or, God forbid, doubled-up round-bale cord, as has happened in emergencies before).

Between Daisy and I, we got the calf out, with a few cotyledons coming away off-coloured indicating that we were indeed too late to bother with the calf. Next job was to get Daisy sat the right way up. More pulling and shoving, now using the cord looped round Daisy's leg. With hands going white as the cord felt like it was going to cut them off, we got her the right way up, facing downhill, and looking like she might fight another day.

I went on my way, having many mouths to feed, and many miles to cover doing it. Taking her a drink and some sweeties later, she was scrawling about, lurching downhill as she tried to get up. Nothing to be done really; either she'd get up, or she wouldn't. Rolling her into the CAT bucket on my own would be quite a feat, but getting it back up the slope would've been miraculous – and then I'd have advanced from having a downer cow sat in the lee of a wall, well down out of the weather, to having a cow stuck upside down in the bucket of a bogged telehandler.

Come Monday morning, after a rough wet night, there was good news and bad. Despite the skin of ice across everything, suggesting I might be going to find a much-loved but very dead cow, she was up and tottering about. The bad news was that I'd wrenched a shoulder which had just about stopped hurting since I last did it damage. So now, while Joe is trying to set a calf on Daisy, I've got a goblin hammering a rusty nail into my right shoulder.

My first venture into publishing

The cows have all been fetched home and are settled into the normal feeding routine. The main feature of my farming life right now, however, is not them, or who is culling what badgers, or how much suckle calves/lamb/milk will be worth next spring. Of much more interest are the problems the bought-in hay is giving me.

See, my pal Russell delivered two lorry loads of very nice June-made seed hay last summer, in big square bales. And very good stuff it is too, verging on 'rocket fuel' quality. Admittedly it's giving me some problems with the wads falling to bits as I carry it about to odd ewes and calves about the place, being very short-fibred brittle stuff – and thereby hangs the real problem. These stubby bits of broken chaff-like stem always end up steadily working their way into my coat, down my shirt, to then make their presence known exactly where a chap doesn't want them.

This would be fine if I could but remember to rid myself of them later in the day. The technique requires a quiet corner, and the dropping of... well, I hardly need draw you a picture do I? But in my hurry, I sometimes forget to attend to such matters before going to meetings, shops, or perchance a meal out. I know you'll say I should change out of my grubby work attire before mixing with polite society, but I seldom do, on general principle.

In the barn *Photograph by Agnes Coaker*

So now there are a number of people who delicately kept a discreet distance from that awful Coaker chap, on the assumption that he must have some awful personal complaint. Some nasty little itch perhaps, perchance picked up at some Oriental house of ill repute (ha! chance would be a fine thing).

The truth is rather less exotic, and I've yet to think of a way to get back at Russell.

As winter bites, various rodents have taken to trying to share my existence. Outside, rats are appearing a bit, and inside a tribe of mice have spent several nights scuttling about the bedroom, determined to keep Alison and I awake. Goodness – but the snapping sound of the trap going off is satisfying, isn't it?

Between the boy's Jack Russell and several traps, we're working on them steadily. I haven't put down any bait yet, preferring to avoid it if I can. Also working at small furry critters is a kestrel that often hunts its way along the side of the valley of a morning. I often disturb it as I return from feeding the cows, flushing it from a perch beside the track with its cargo of fresh vole.

My first venture into publishing has been quite an eye opener (*All the usual bullocks*). You see, with no one beating at the door to make me an offer to take the matter forward, I simply hired in the requisite operatives, and organised it myself.

While it took a bit of time to get everything in place, and I then had to front the sum required to fund operations, it's now largely set up. The distribution takes a bit of thinking about, but the mound of cardboard boxes steadily shrinks.

Various larger concerns have angled to stitch me up, but I'm not rising to their rather complex bait, smelling a different sort of rat in their 'small print'. Certain locals have been able to spend a happy evening or two trying to find themselves hidden in the text – for many of them have indeed strayed onto these pages in various poor disguises over the years. Most are happy to recognise their aliases I might add, and no writs have arrived as yet.

There was a bit of a flap when a copy was sent to... um... a 'VIP' household, and it was pointed out that that, should the occupant choose to pick it up, he might well recognise himself therein somewhere and take offence. I can't get that exercised about it. As I replied, anyone taking offence would have to have set their filter way, way too low.

I have signed several copies, although again my habits often mean my grubby signature is smudged with varying combinations of sheep paint/blood/iodine/tannin/amniotic fluid or diesel, depending on what rustic task I've been applying myself to of late. I think it all adds to the authenticity!

Phones down

The raging storms that first week of January brought down a tree in the village, along with half the phone lines. We didn't notice til the evening, because we were busy shovelling cattle through the crush TB testing in the deluge. Being reliant on communications down a bit of copper wire for all sorts of things, Alison was then soon out at the end of the road to get reception with a mobile, and report this incident. (It is fair to assume that we weren't the first to report it, either.)

Now despite what you might have come to think over the years, I am a reasonable and patient man. I know quite well that managing repairs after storms like that must be devilishly difficult. And so I was delighted to get the message that BT would have us connected up by the end of the next day. (I didn't listen very carefully to the exact details Alison reported, not listening being my default position.)

When this repair didn't actually materialise when it was promised, I took a turn at chasing it up. So I drove to the end of the road, to spend '40p a minute' listening to a recorded message, with various options to follow. Before the options were revealed, the recording was very keen to tell me that BT are sponsoring the Olympics – what? Is that instead of fixing my phone line? – and that 'this call may be recorded for training purposes'. This was all spoken nice and slow, so I could get the full benefit of listening to my 40p a minute tick away.

It was seemingly impossible to speak to a human being, which did rather beg the question why the call was being recorded for training purposes? Eventually, tapping in the number of the landline that I was reporting a fault on revealed to the machine that I am a 'broadband customer'. The wretched thing then delighted in informing me that I could look up the problem on their website. Sadly, it didn't tell me how I was going to do this, seeing as… all together now… 'The phone lines are down.'

BT were also very keen that I then dial another '40p a minute' line to report my broadband fault, but by now I was recalling some of what my beloved had ranted, after she'd played this game. These lines all lead to similar dead ends, telling us to go back to the first number.

Each day we were promised the fault was scheduled to be rectified by the close of play the following day (although reporting a domestic number suffering the same fault led to promises of repair sometime next week); that is, a bloke would come out with a ladder and a screwdriver to hook up my 'business' line – and that to the pub. Then someone else – or possibly the same man albeit looking a bit harassed by then – would return a week later to connect all the houses about the hamlet. Hmm. I'm led to assume that BT are lying about this for some reason, which displeases me.

For the record, I have nothing but praise for the poor fellas scurrying about the countryside in the transits. They tend to be practical, not afraid of going up ladders in the rain, and are usually on the ball. However, I take great exception to the weasels sat in a warm office charging me for lies. I would very much like to be able to do business with them on a one-to-one basis.

Anyway. After some days of various communication difficulties (quite apart from 'Bloggs the builder' wanting to know where his flipping beams are, the kids are presumed to have internet hook-up to do their homework, and the Revenue rather expected Alison to return some 'return' or other on line) we are now back, dangling at the end of a copper wire once more.

Do recall this when you hear about some fabulous plan to roll out instant broadband to every last shepherd's hut on the hill, and that some rural taskforce is going to make everything wonderful and rosy. All we actually need is a moderately bright lad with a ladder.

The 'real' Olympics

I've been thinking about these here Olympics. First off, I've got to admit I'm already long since fed up hearing about them. The basic idea is OK, I suppose. And if it stuck to that principle, ie just a competition held to see who can run fastest or jump highest… that'd be fine. And if you're interested in that sort of thing, I suppose you might want to go along and watch. Fair enough. Somehow, though, it's mushroomed out of all proportion, to the point now where punters might very well be prepared to go along to the opening/closing ceremony, but not catch any of the sporting events themselves.

That says everything about the Olympics for me. I acknowledge that my position may be influenced by an almost total disinterest in sport per se. If I've got a few spare calories of energy left at the end of a day, I'm more inclined to go and bang up some logs, or shovel up some muck, than go jogging. It's not that I'm uncompetitive – far from it – only I see a rather bigger game to take part in. (And as a pal once pointed out, it's just as well so few competitors realise what the nature of the game is; they'd be so much harder to beat if they did.)

Although I don't anticipate many accolades in the 'sport' I pursue (or medals for that matter), I absolutely give it my best shot. You can judge my performance as you nail the lid down.

Back to the formal games themselves. There don't seem to be any events at which you and I might excel. This hardly seems fair, given the remarkable feats of physical prowess and dexterity we sometimes display. I realise that the problem is simply in the terms of reference. If they would but move the 'goalposts' a bit, as it were, we'd be right in there on Team GB. What we need is….

Track and field
- 50m feedsack carry, dodging 75 in-lamb ewes
- 100m 'ear-tag inspector' evasion dash
- 200m 'evade the newly calved cow' hedge hurdle
- 4 x 400m 'fresh-spool-of-bale-cord' relay
- 1500m 'remembered I left diesel tap running'
- Pursuit of runaway bulling heifer half marathon (exit stadium, follow bank of Thames upstream to Tower Bridge, wade/swim across under bridge, back down far bank. Various parks and gardens will be included, along with two more river crossings. Tail-enders in field will find race timed to leave them on rising tide)
- The 10yd 'dropped lump hammer' hop
- Hurling the expired lamb (standing start)
- Toss the non-starting chainsaw (two revolutions in nets allowed)
- 24-hour SFP deadline scramble (an office-bound event)
- Bantamweight bullock wrestling (dehorning iron supplied)
- Open class spray-suit-adorning challenge
- Freestyle 'ramblers in the hayfields' yodelling

On the shooting range
- 30-second scramble into the bushes, clutching a brace of his lordship's pheasants
- Visiting-rare-breed-ram-in-mule-hog's skeet (points jointly awarded for shooting skill and use of vernacular language)

In the equine arena
- Five-a-side feral mare gather (quads not permitted)
- Open two-man foal branding
- The 'Other Pentathlon' *This more realistic event will include 'catching the unbroken mount', swimming from deep pond into which it subsequently throws you, chasing it five miles on a mountain bike, shooting the bliddy thing dead from 300 yards, and lastly, 'the indefinite run' upon discovery that you were given the wrong horse, and its former owner would like a real serious word.*

In the pool (differing from usual games by contents of pool, to be refilled with 'fluid' of slightly heavier viscosity)

- Skipping across the crust lagoon dash (NB Only the Gold medal will be awarded. It is assumed that once the first competitor has made his/her way across, thus breaking the crust, the rest of the field may find themselves in a different competition. Survivors issued with runners-up medals)
- The 20ft 'stogged' ewe recovery, no aids allowed
- The 'strimmed-wasp-nest' freestyle dive (filtered snorkels permitted)
- 25ft freestyle swim, dragging strop out to milking cow treading water in mid-lagoon

Clearly these are events which would have far more entertainment value. Someone text that nice young Coe lad, and I'll go have a word with Boris.

Black walnut

With a chill still in the air, I've been exercising that arch contradiction of using a computer beside a blazing open fire. I suppose I could turn it around and write this diary on a clay tablet by the warmth of some clever geothermal ground source radiator, but where's the fun it that. Besides, I'm not sure how I'd email the clay tablet to the editor.

For added flavour, much of the fuel tonight has been waste chips and ends of the black walnut root plate I hacked up a couple of weeks back. Various slabs are off to make shotgun and rifle butts, and figured coffee tables, but other chunks are warming my toes. Technically, it must be about the most expensive firewood I could use, but hey! let's push the boat out.

The American black walnut deserves some thought. It is, obviously enough, an American native, only having been introduced here about 400 years ago: gardener John Tradescant reputedly had one growing in South Lambeth in 1633. This compares with what we'd call English walnut (which is nothing of the sort, but a native of central Asia, likely delivered to our shores with the Romans, via the Greeks; they thought the nuts were good for the brains, cos they looked a bit like the old grey matter, but then they had all sorts of wacky theories).

The nuts of the black walnut are also edible, although it is the timber which interests your scribe most. When fresh sawn it is a sickly greeny colour, streaked with black. As the surface dries it quickly attains a black-brown hue, with an unexpected and unlikely hint of purple running through it. While not just as valuable as its European counterpart – which tends to a more tobacco-brown colour – it is still highly prized. Due to difficulty transplanting it (with a fragile tap root) it's seldom grown over here commercially, even though in favoured sites it grows to an immense size. The root plate I've just dismembered was dug out from the grounds of Killerton House, after the tree had been condemned and felled. ('Oh' said my old Mum, on my return, 'I used to go to parties there when I was a little girl.' I have to remember she fell on rather hard times coming here.)

The main trunk alone had 22 feet of clean timber, averaged over three feet in diameter, and had made a trunk worth several thousand in just about a hundred years. Despite some fag-packet maths suggesting that growing the things on a commercial scale the return might be very respectable, I only know one forest owner who is pursuing the theory.* Unfortunately, cute as that man is, his clay land is much better suited to oak, and I worry he's flogging a dead nag with his walnuts.

Back to the tree from Killerton. I was unsuccessful in buying the main stick, but did secure the root and some big limbs, and had been sitting on the bigger chunk of this treasure for about 15 years when we finally broke it down. It is perfectly durable, and I wasn't disappointed. I don't generally bother with walnut roots, as the bother is far more than the return, but this one was immense, and rippled beautifully as it went beneath the ground. Result.

*If you're going to pursue such arcane interests, I advise careful research into your soil's capacity, and do watch the provenance of the stock you plant. They're not all as wont to make such clean upstanding sticks as that one was. This advice applies to many of life's endeavours. In fact, we could probably stretch the metaphor to cover almost everything! I'll return to matching provenance with conditions another day.

Recent freeze-up

The frost last week brought some ups and downs.

Obviously, getting water to everything can be a chore, although we got away without too much fuss this time. I'm very chuffed to be able to boast that some of the pipes carefully buried under some new troughs a couple of years ago stayed fluid (we'll neatly gloss over those that failed). Pulling the wrap off frozen bales isn't especially fun either, nor digging out the strings, which can't be sensibly done in gloves, but hey-ho. Then there was a heart-stopping moment while feeding cows. I'd trundled the loader tractor out to a round feeder, with silage bale high in the air. As I turned a corner on the frozen gloop, the outside front wheel punched unexpectedly through into the mire below. 'Yikes!' I exclaimed, as we nearly went over. Conversation at the public bar of the Hefted Goat reveals other chums have had similar experiences and made like exclamations.

In the sawmill there's been solidified bandsaw lubricant, and packs of beams frozen together for days. When you prise them apart, they go sliding off in an alarming manner. The iron bed of the saw I work sucks the warmth out of bare fingers in very few minutes, meaning I've had to adorn myself with gloves. I don't like this one bit, as anything likely to snag in a piece of wood raises the threat of not being able to count to 10 in years to come. Equally though, not being able to feel your pinkies can lead to mishaps as well.

The plus sides of the freeze-up? When avoiding such heart-in-mouth-tippy-over incidents, at least I could zip around the deep frozen tundra elsewhere, the tractor making no mess at all. The livestock were quite happy for the most part. Some of the outlying cows didn't like negotiating the bone-hard irregular frozen mud around the feeders, and I can't blame them. I think, on balance though, I prefer the jagged ankle traps to the porridge the cows and I negotiate most of the winter. I am minded that 13 months ago, when we had weeks of it coupled to a big pile of snow, the novelty wore a bit thin. Eventually, last winter, one or two cows had ripped the hoofy bit off their dewclaws, which didn't look very pretty. It didn't seem to worry them overly, and they grew back fine.

On the subject of cows' feet, one South Devon has required a bit more TLC than usual – admittedly the 'usual' being a cursory glance that they're all up and noshing. She is the youngest of a bunch, and not carrying much spare cover, so is always at the back of the queue. See, while cows are generally very easy-going creatures, and like nothing more than to stand around stuffing their faces, to then loaf about the rest of the day cudding, they do always maintain a strict hierarchy. Big cow is boss, and woe betide small cow who steps in front of her. Anyhow, I know a more diligent man would've moved this little cow somewhere where she wasn't at the bottom of the pecking order, but it hadn't got to the top of my list when she started hanging back from the feeder. Then she was favouring a foot, which quickly started lighting up the warning signals. Sure enough the leg started to swell up, so after everything was fed, Joe went to investigate further. He found her sulking in the gorse bushes by the river, and refusing to walk the half-mile home for examination. Not to be perturbed, Joe dived into the gorse, and got her foot up. Hey presto, he spotted the end of a bent piece of wire, and managed to tease it out of the sole of her hoof before she could hop away.

Now I have pulled a shiny neat two-inch galvanised nail from the hoof of a South Devon in similar circumstances – ALWAYS pick up those dropped nails and bits of wire boys and girls – and that one went on her way never looking back. But this cow has needed dosing up with antibiotics to stop anything nasty creeping further up her leg.

We got her a bit closer to home, and the infection that had got in has now exited just above her hoof. The swelling has gone right down again, and she's putting some weight on it, looking a bit happier with her lot. We'll see.

Chin up, evenings are pulling out.

SPRING 2012

Farmer X's panic button

I think it's time we caught up with a few old chums.

Long-time readers will recall 'Farmer X' retired to a bit of off land down the road, handing the reins to the very capable 'Farmer X Jnr'. Senior, now sadly widowed, pootles about, minding the group of cows in his charge, standing in on the main farm when required, or arsing about in some woodlands he bought to keep his hand in. He's not one to sit around, and still does a harder day's graft than many half his age. This is often deep in the woods, clutching dangerous power tools, and hence his family have prevailed upon him, in recognition of his advancing years, to wear some kind of panic button.

Recently we got a rather frantic call from Junior. Firstly, he had a heifer calving, which was going Pete Tong, and could we help his Mrs and the vet, as 'Dad's panic button has gone off' and Junior felt obliged to rush to his aid. I was away from home when the alarm went up, so stockman Joe was quickly despatched to help with the calving.

By the time I returned from my excursion, Junior had been all over the parish, becoming increasingly worried, before finally ascertaining that the old man had (a) gone off to the far end of someone else's woods without telling Junior, (b) hit this panic button by accident while turning his phone off, and (c) not thought to report in that he was perfectly happy, felling timber a mile in from the road.

I believe the only real danger to his person was what Junior was going to do to him when he finally caught up with him. The heifer had to be Caesared, too late for the calf, but heifer saved.

Then there is a lady farmer of my acquaint, who has made several guest appearances herein while not actually being named. We'll christen her 'Flossie', seeing as it will annoy her so.

Being an old friend – close on 30 years now m'dear – Flossie was delighted to hear about my book. Indeed she took it upon her cultured self to purchase a significant number of copies as Christmas presents for her wide circle of chums. Now this circle includes one or two old flames of mine (Alison is well aware of this, and holding out that one of them will reappear to claim me). In a careless moment, when ordering another 10 copies by email, Flossie included her annotated notes regarding recipients. They cryptically – and speculatively I might add – indicated either 'Did' or 'Didn't' (and one 'DEFINITELY didn't') beside each name. I returned the order, altering certain parts of the list to read 'Didn't… yet!'

And, of course, there's that scoundrel Egbert. Passing the out-of-the-way hamlet, lost amid unclassified roads in the backcountry, where Egbert keeps his abode, I noticed most of the former farmworker's and miner's cottages are for sale once more. It seemed like most of them had only changed hands 10 minutes ago, yet estate agents' signs sprout up once more, like some seasonal hedgerow bloom.

I managed to track Egbert down in the public bar of The Strangled Ferret a few days later, to see if he could shed some light on matters. You see, although his interests are ostensibly centred on the price ratio of baled silage and rolled barley against that of two-year-old bullocks, or whether the Brigadier is going to let him graze those lower meadows this year, after last year's unfortunate incident when Horace's Charolais steers got into the Brigadier's new greenhouse, there are all manner of peripheral interests that catch Egbert's eye.

He will always be keen to know whose wedding had to be hurriedly brought forward a month or two, or why someone else is suddenly shifting a lot of young cattle through the store market the same week as that new tractor went back. It's not that he's nosey, you understand; it's just that he cares deeply for the wider community, and likes to be kept abreast of what's happening. He can't help himself.

But this was clearly a more subtle matter altogether, for while Egbert's concern for the rural community he belongs to is far-reaching, and taken quite seriously, his interest in the urban resettlers is rather less focussed.

As I arrived, I found our mischievous hero quietly baiting some poor blow-in who was trying to munch his way through a vegetarian cutlet at the bar. The man was wearing designer labels, a bemused expression, and an increasingly queasy colour, as his 'new best friend' discussed favourite cures for constipation in bullocks (which I happen to know full well the beggar was making up as he went along). I managed to head him off before he got onto current fashions in castration techniques, as I don't think his victim was going to go the distance.

Filling his flagon (and should you wish to ply him with the demon brew, by all means leave the wherewithal with me and I'll see it gets to him), we speculated… what on earth must he say to these people, that they up sticks and move on so quickly?

They arrive, he reckons, after viewing these properties on a sunny June afternoon, and consequently having paid a price more like a telephone number. Then the rain, mud and fog-delayed-commute-times start to sap the enthusiasm, and quickly they're off again. Few of them ever notice old Egbert, and he admits he can't be bothered with learning their names any more. When his tribe and others locally have been muddling along in the same parish for some centuries, he can't really grasp the newcomers' constant throughput.

To be fair, if newcomers stick around for a year or two, Egbert usually gives them a chance. Sadly, he confides as we drain our flagons, most of them still subsequently fail the 'bullshit detector' test.

We went on our way a little older, but not much wiser.

Swaling

After a dry spell, one day last week just on the cusp of being misty found us out in a gurt patch of gorse with a box of matches. The enclosure is 40 acres or so, and is partly infested with both European – big – gorse, and the smaller 'tame furze'. For good measure its topside, which runs up to the common, is awash with raffia-like dead molinia grass. The common stretches for miles, and is equally inflammable.

Firing the newtake is very chancy business, with the risk of a fire leaping onto the common. In this day of minimal-stocking-density enviro-agreements, it's a double-bubble situation. There's not enough livestock to eat the vegetation, raising the risk of uncontrollable wildfires. These in turn risk the cancellation of the schemes – and the cheques they attract.

Anyway, with a slight breeze blowing downhill, away from the common, and just a touch of damp about, we reckoned we could keep matters in check. It may seem obvious, but wildfires travel uphill, and downwind, much faster than the opposites, so conditions were optimal.

So I dutifully phoned in my swaling plans to everyone on the official checklist. Well, not everyone, because the police force number was unobtainable. I didn't pursue the matter, as I wasn't sure what the Old Bill were going to do. Read the advancing fire front its rights? I'm joking, of course; we let the law know when there is likely to be a traffic problem.

I gave my start – 'As soon as I get off the phone, guv' – and stop times, grid reference, confirmed that I had staff on hand and assured everyone that I knew what I was doing. The latter might have been a bit of an embellishment, but I do know how to strike a match!

Eventually, Joe and I were able to grab a shovel each, and the 'smudge pot', and set off. Said smudge pot is an open-top paint tin, punched with vent holes, wired to the end of a three-foot batten. Stuffed with dead grass/ dried cow dung/rags, or anything else to act as a wick, and topped up with jungle juice, it will burn for half an hour or so, saving all that faffing about with the matchbox.

Conditions were perfect for such a risky site, and we were able to fire a large 'backburn' firebreak in the dead grass, before we considered the gorse. If molinia is too dry, trying to beat it out with a shovel or a flappy beater just fans little wisps of burning grass out in six directions, starting six new fires (much like trying to kill the Hydra). On this occasion, though, the fire front just sulked along, and was easily steered and stopped. Admittedly, the burn didn't go as deep as I'd have liked, but that is the nature of the beast.

Once there was clear burnt ground on the dangerous sides, we looked to the gorse. But it was getting late, so we lit no more, and adjourned. The

following day was a little bit drier, with the wind still blowing away from the common. Leaving Joe in the yard, loading poop with one eye on the mobile phone, I went back and lit around the outsides of the remaining block with impudence.

Swaling gone a bit wrong!

It is a bit of a rush, touching the tame little flame in the pot to a clump of dead white grass. Just the faintest of an orange tongue licks the vegetation, hesitating for a moment before creeping rapidly into the neighbouring gorse. With a crisp crackling, and billowing white smoke, the fire takes. In just moments, the harmless lick of orange has turned into a head-height conflagration, tightening the skin on your cheeks. The bulk of dry matter shrinks as the fire grows. Once it is travelling with the breeze, driving moisture out of further bushes as it goes, the mass of flame grows and grows in volume. In amongst dense stands of gorse, especially that which had suffered in the bone-cracking frost the Christmas before last, it starts to roar. The crackling amplifies to a crashing sound, filled with a muffled crumpling, as sap boils and gases rupture gorse stems. Flames leap 20 feet in the air, consuming everything in their way. Dead gorse, live gorse, clumps of whortleberry matted with wiry thin dead grasses, even thorn and rowan saplings peeking through the brush, all consumed and converted into a spiralling cloud of embers carried aloft in the vortex.

And then, with its fuel supply exhausted, it dies away again in moments, leaving a downwind snow of ash, and forgotten views into the boulders in the undergrowth.

In coming weeks, as weather warms and new growth starts to poke through, the livestock will trample through the charred residue, covering themselves with soot and opening up the habitat once more.

Lambing and calving

I've mostly made it through another lambing and calving on the hill, although it was a bit testing in the cold April rain. I do enjoy both the multiplication of new lives, and the challenge of giving them as good a chance as I can. But I enjoyed rather less the constant shuttling outfits into cover when things went awry.

Highlights this year have included several unexpectedly successful fosterings – always a great relief – and dealing with a three-headed sheep. This latter wasn't some mutated Schmallenburg case, but rather an elderly Scotch ewe with a pair of lambs trying to exit simultaneously. One of them was even waving his little trotter at me, as his mum and I played tag round the hillside and they nodded along in time. You wouldn't think a gravid ewe would feel much like sprinting about at such a moment, but you know what sheep are.

Anyhow, once secured, I posted one of her little cherubs back indoors so I could extract the other, then the former. All good, except that they were never going to get a hold of those enormous teats, and the whole outfit needed recovering back to the yard for further ministrations –and a course of antibiotics. (An old hand told me once he 'likes to 'ave a maid 'elp at lambin', cuz they generally remember to give the ewe the injection before the beggar dies.')

This particular ewe's udder wasn't the only problem one. There is plenty of milk about, but also a number of older ewes with overly big teats, which has led to a lot of shepherding work.

Whilst bent over another case, I got thinking about the breeding of those afflicted. I've narrowed the problem down to the ram/rams responsible, finding it to be none other than my favourite homebred post-FMD bruiser 'Git' and a pair of his sons I used extensively. Once their daughters hit seven or eight years, an increasing number are now requiring additional labour input.

On balance, I suppose their general longevity is to be applauded – indeed, I'd expect nothing less from such a wild-eyed hardbitten strain. But the added labour cost is very much against my ethos.

John and lamb

This in turn has had me thinking about these here scientific scoring systems. You all know what a Luddite I am about such go-ahead methods, infamous as I am for buying a South Devon bull because the breeder said what a lovely cow the dam was, or various hues of Riggit Galloway bulls chosen because they have a pleasing colour pattern across their backs. Rams are often quite deliberately sourced from 'feral' unmanaged flocks, and if I could get a bull calf off the uninhabited Orkney island of Swona, with its feral herd of cattle, I certainly would.

But I'm curious now. Do any of the initials and acronyms quoted stand for the calculated effects of eventual udder confirmation in the aged granddaughters of a breeding Scotch ram? I rather doubt it, and shall continue to place my trust in traditional methods of stock selection.

This does remind me of a very steady family I know, whose Scotch ewes are legendary in their thrift and longevity on high ground. The old granddad selected a yearling ram for me once, for which I paid well. Some years after the old chap passed on I told his son that I had just sold this sheep, which had done me a lot of good and was now hale and hearty and in late middle age. The son berated me for letting such an animal go... when they're still hale at a good age, that's when you really start to value them. Another ram, which I still have, was sired by a nine-year-old tup, and one of my favourite ewes is now 13 and going well. Somewhere I've got pictures of a working Scotch ram aged 17.

Mind, all this careful selection doesn't always work. My dear Dad had carefully weeded out a whole family of South Devons who had behavioural issues. 'Glancer' was the name given to the dam line. A few years later, when I was in my teens and wanting to run a few cows of my own, I bought in a miscellaneous bunch of South Devon heifer calves to rear on. One of these came from a local herd, and after the sale the vendor assured me – with an odd smile – that the calf was out of a cow he'd bought from my old man. I told Dad this when I got the calf home, and his face fell. Did this calf have a bit of a long narrow face? It did – because that man bought the last of the Glancer cows. Sure enough, two years later when she had produced her first offspring, I was escorted from her field as fast as a teenager could run.

I soon weeded her out of my embryonic herd, having learned some practical lessons in inheritable traits and hill farmers. (Mostly that no one will sell you their best heifers; or if they do, whatever rubbish must they breed themselves?)

I'm happy to share these tips with you, beyond price as they may be; merely fill me with ale when we are next met.

Planting Les Branfield

Here, I could've saved the Government millions on the new Met Office super-computer by telling them exactly when the wet and cold would return. It was bound to occur just as my lambs and calves started popping out, and it did.

These activities happen mostly alfresco at Coaker Hall, in the healthy fresh air. As you might imagine, it's been a bit up and down. Last Monday was a shocker, and knocked down several lambs and a calf, and we've had two or three sessions not much better since. I have managed to fetch in various outfits in time to sort out crises, and that makes me feel very farmery and organised. But I don't get it all right, which makes me feel rather less wholesome.

I had to arrange lambing cover last week to go and plant an old pal in Hawkridge churchyard. Les Branfield was a lifelong farmer – and would've no doubt related to all of the above – and left us at the good age of 78. I was one of many who couldn't fit in the little stone-built church on the southern edge of Exmoor, so I stood in the sun remembering him. One of his sons, Layland, asked those attending to each think of a little story about Les, and share it with someone else present. I couldn't stay for the bun-fight, so here's a couple for you Layland.

Some time ago, I travelled to Exmoor by motorbike on a jolly. Unfortunately, I met a pool of diesel on the road en route, and slid off into the hedge. Apart from holing my knee, I snapped the end off the old Triumph's clutch cable. Bumping into Les later, I told him my tale. He chewed on his lip for a moment, and told me to drop in on my way home. Sure enough, taking me into possibly the most cluttered workshop in Christendom – his 'glory hole' – he rummaged around in the gleanings from many a farm sale, before proudly – triumphantly even! – pulling out the wherewithal to fix the cable there and then. What a star.

Then later, when Alison and I were courting, we spent a happy week lodging with Les and Ruth. Les took it upon himself to show us the local sights. I'm not sure all B&B guests got this service, but it was highly enlightening. Included, as I recall, was the churchyard. In fact, he asked me if that lovely yew tree was worth anything. I said I couldn't value it as it was probably sacred, quite possibly predating the church. He thought about this, and agreed that was likely the case. I can only speculate what would've happened if I said it was worth a few quid!

He was a lovely man, and it was a privilege to have known him.

Opera

As you well know, my idea of refined pastimes might not align with everyone's, and my musical interests have quite openly included, of late, critical analysis of the social impact of early Wurzels' material. Not that I'm parochial in this. When I'm tapping away I listen to anything from Holst to Rage Against The Machine, from sun-scorched dusty Aboriginal tunes through to swamp-infested Cajun music.

My educated cousin Al knows all this, and has been trying to improve me by exposing me to culture once more. To this end he and my lovely cousin-in-law, Judith, procured tickets for some bash, and instructed Alison to have me cleanly scrubbed and ready for the off at an appointed time. Misunderstanding, I assumed we were off to some wedding function as we were apparently attending 'The Marriage of Figaro'. It turns out that this is something called 'The Opera' which, as you may know, is where posh people sit and let some fat bird warble at them all evening, and very carefully pretend to enjoy the experience.

Things kicked off well enough with a meal in some trendy gaff nearby, where cast concrete and un-planed oak made up many of the fittings. I approve, although I hadn't appreciated that the great and the good go for such stark functionality. I did rather let the side down by attracting the eye of the serving wench with the 'come to attention' whistle. It works fine with the wife, kids and collies, but goes down less well with waitresses. The nosh was cheap enough (although refined folk apparently need fewer calories than the great unwashed).

At the appointed hour, we ambled round the corner. The venue included yet more mass concrete structures, with lots of glass. Throngs of punters milled about trying to find their seats, being frightfully genteel in suits and smart frocks. I was attired in my traditional costume, and was merely frightful. I rather suspect mine were the only steel toecap boots in the auditorium.

Cousin Al could only afford tickets right up the front, but this did allow me to stand up and look behind us before kick-off, to see who I could wave at. This is always good sport, and in any given West Country crowd I usually spot someone I can later have a yarn with, often even doing a bit of business through the evening. Curiously I didn't recognise anyone, except possibly a geezer in a suit who made eye contact, but I think I might only know him from the other side of the 'bench'. I was clearly in some counter culture.

And so to this opera business. What happens is this: a band sit in an open cellar below the stage and thrash their way through a load of classical music, while a cast of portly singers act out a wafer-thin plot by shrieking it in some foreign language.

Absolutely blinking fascinating.

There were electronic subtitles displaying translations for novices, but sadly they were hung somewhere aloft in the ceiling, so I quickly cricked my neck trying to follow proceedings. Everyone seemed to be yearning for a bit of unrequited how's-your-father with everyone else. Between quizzing Judith and reading up in the programme, I ascertained that the music was written by an Austrian, the words by an Italian – in Italian – about a story set in Spain. This was being performed by the Welsh National Opera, which included a Uruguayan for good measure. The singing occasionally found its mark, but was generally let down by the warbling and shrieking. I did some homework, and apparently there is absolutely no indication that the writers of either music or words required this affectation; it merely seems to have developed. And a bit like the king's new suit, no one has the balls to say it's rubbish.

In fairness, I should observe that the company seem to have been filling the hall with lungpower alone, which must be quite a trick. The music itself was very good in parts – it was a bloke called Mozart wot wrote it apparently – and I'd say the invisible band bashed it out pretty well. And Figaro's bird was played by the comparatively diminutive Elizabeth Watts, who shrieked rather less but could still belt out a good tune. She was expressive, had very satisfactory locomotion – in the eye of a jaundiced old hill farmer – and quite stole the show.

Anyway. Don't think I'm ungrateful; I very much enjoyed the experience, if for all the wrong reasons. Now Al and Judith have treated us with this jolly, I'm wondering how to repay the kindness. Al did drop by when we were TB testing in January's gales, but his lovely wife missed that particular cultural outing. Now let me see…

Ladies' tug-of-war

We all have our fantasies. These might range from mundane speculations about what it would be like to lift the County Championship with your favourite Lesser Crested Snapping Guinea Pig, or perhaps – having been able to persuade Fido not to savage the clutch of startled mule hogs this time – to win the local sheepdog trials, through to rather more unfathomable matters. Some of us have more ambitious secret thoughts, like how startled would everyone be to discover that old Ms Figglethin's solicitors and Land Registry had finally sorted things out, and that, after cheerily mowing her lawn of a Sunday afternoon for a couple of summers, you are the sole beneficiary, inheriting three-quarters of the parish, including the farm rented by that cussed old beggar whose cows you've been milking these last 17 years.

I suppose, with less imagination, it might be a simple as crassly pretending to see your numbers come up on the euro-millions lottery jackpot. Goodness, but what fun you can have just thinking about all the stuff 143 million euros would buy. Half of Greece for a start. (Naturally enough, you'll gloss over that you need to have bought a ticket in the first place. After all, we're considering fantasy worlds here.)

Then there are the rather more 'earthly' fantasies to consider, if not in too fine a detail. I give them little attention myself nowadays, having somehow found myself married to a rather beautiful woman, who can not only raise kids and calve cows, but understands SFP forms and cattle movement rules. If she'd only get the hang of sheep shearing and running the sawmill, we'd really be cooking with gas.

I suppose, to enter the spirit of things, I might wonder if she needs some help. If I were allowed to hire, say, Cameron Diaz as my PA, it would certainly keep me out of Alison's hair. And, quite possibly, if poor Cameron was finding it a bit of a struggle keeping up, we could find her a job-share stand-in. (I'm not a monster you know). Salma Hayek comes to mind, if you're going to press me on this irksome task.

I admit this all shows a predictable lack of imagination on my part. Highly regrettable I know, especially compared to the fantasy I heard about last week.

While leaning on our sticks at the ringside of Midden Bottom District Show, as the St John Ambulance chaps tidied up the fallout from the Boy Scouts' Formation Skateboard Leapfrogging display, a crony and I were passing the time of day. Addled by the sun, or possibly dazed from a long day on his feet, my pal wasn't thinking too carefully, and let slip an admission. While trundling about in his loader tractor, or laboriously shovelling something boring – and he farms a particularly hard bit of ground, with rather more 'fuzz and rocks' than anything else, which I'm sure makes for a deeper line of contemplation – this rural sage admitted one of his favourite daydreams is to put thought to the make-up of the Dartmoor All-Stars Ladies' Tug of War Team.

Straight away I could see the attraction in this particular diversion. Team members would have to have the ability to dig their heels in (quite possibly equating to contenders' likely capacity to help dehorn the calves or dip the ewes), as well as providing a beneficial mass when keeping one warm nights.

Obviously, my pal had made a head start, and his 'A team' was already mostly ready to go – in his head at least. I was playing catch up, but had to concur that he had a pretty good line-up. Several of his choices would be a cert, whoever was picking this team.

Thinking about it, my friend is just a year or two older than myself, and richer in life's experience. It might be he's now judging such requirements a little differently. I think my own selection might be more suitable to the 'Upper Dart Ladies' Rugby Team', which might be reflected in a lower combined weight, albeit with a bit more length of leg.

In fact, some of the team selection work is already done. You see, a popular spectator sport locally is to be found at the Midden Bottom District Show, in form of the Ladies' Bale Tossing finals. That always draws a rapt crowd for some reason, emptying the beer tent in fact. You can keep yer beach volleyball mate: these are contestants who can fling a bale, and there'd be rich pickings for the dream team once you get to the quarter-final stages. I must make some notes next September.

Anyway, I bring you these thoughts not just to help you focus on your own daydreams, but to realise it isn't just you!

Flying into meetings

Having cause to be at the other end of the country recently, a couple of colleagues and I hopped on an early morning flight with one of those cheapo airlines. It wasn't the worst experience I've ever had, although woe would surely betide you if you failed to make things very easy indeed for 'Sleazyflight'. I believe there were a host of little surcharges for the unwary, but you generally get what you pay for in life.

I wasn't going to go, having other commitments, but was prevailed upon at the last minute. By then I'd missed the cheapest of the deals, but heigh-ho.

I allowed my computer operative to book my tickets once she'd cooked tea and helped the kids with homework. I don't like to let her feel left out. Then I had a query regarding some detail which couldn't be answered on the website, and I eventually tracked down a phone number. That took me to a nice lady whose Indian accent I couldn't really understand

(and, even if I could, I don't think she knew much about the workings of UK airlines: fascinating).

And now I notice unbidden messages keep popping up on my screen from the self-same airline. Sly little beggars. They somehow retain your info and try to sell you more stuff. I'm informed by my betters that this involves something called 'cookies', although they don't look like the chocolate chip variety.

Come the day – or rather the 'very early morning' – we intrepid travellers found ourselves in a regional airport, where parking costs nearly as much as flying. After an industrial-strength coffee with the rather lovely Ola – a very sweet Pole – we made our way through check-in. As you probably know, nowadays this involves X-rays and searches, looking for Semtex socks with which you might blow a hole in the plane, or sharpened bits of steel to prod the pilot into flying you to Cuba or Beirut. (The latter seems pretty unlikely, since I doubt if 'Sleazyflight' allow the pilot an eggcup more fuel than he needs.*)

I rarely get searched, despite my decidedly dodgy appearance. In fact I was principally interested in getting some kip on the plane, rather than issuing my demands or crashing it into the Palace of Westminster. One of my colleagues, however – who, I think it's fair to say, looks like what he'd really be interested in is his carpet slippers, a comfy chair and his paper – apparently always gets searched… always. I'm not aware that he's caused Special Branch any worries in his long-distant youth, but I'd be pretty surprised if he'd be up to anything too nefarious nowadays. And sure enough, some security guard pulled our man aside to carefully frisk him.

Anyway, we made our destination in time to fulfil our allotted tasks, planning to catch the evening flight home. I'd love to tell you the details of our day, but that would rather spoil the vague illusion of jet-setting importance. In fact it was all rather mundane, and once dealt with it was a taxi back to the airport that end where, sure enough, one of our party was frisked once more. He wouldn't mind, he admits, if it was some smiley maid doing this frisking, but it's always a plank-faced bloke.

This time, to while away a few minutes in the departure lounge while Biggles rewound the elastic band, I fell into conversation with some chap flogging tickets to win a rather swish Aston Martin. Being a natural sceptic and relatively quick with maths, I soon raised questions pertaining to the number of tickets sold and details of the draw, which revealed that the odds were somewhat stacked against me. He optimistically kept up the patter, especially when I revealed that I was heavily into gambling. Sadly, I explained, his odds didn't strike me as much fun as, say, punting a few grand on a parcel of oak trunks, or a pedigree bull I fancied. (Or, for that matter, typing out the mundane doings of what's caught my eye this week, hoping the editor will give it the nod.)

Mind, the next traveller he snared – a spotty youth in pinstripes – was evidently mug enough, so good luck to him. And as they say, taking a fool's money is fine… the world has an endless supply.

On the subject of airlines and aviation fuel. A pal of mine once flew to Canada on an airline which very soon after went bust in a big way. He knew nothing of this while in their care, and couldn't understand why they made a brief unscheduled stop in St Johns, Newfoundland. There he saw, out of the cabin window, a fuel bowser pull alongside the plane; and, plain as day, a uniformed member of the flight crew hand over cash for the fuel. The implication is that their credit was no good, and they left Heathrow with just enough juice to get across the pond to the first 'service station'. Crikey Biggles, that was a narrow squeak!

Diesel fit

One of the perennial bugbears of writing columns – as I do for various publications – is the constant threat of repeating myself. There are scurrilous suggestions that when I'm pressed for time, and an editor is breathing down the inbox, I might be tempted to simply dig into a file of older material, and re-date a piece. This is absolutely not the case, and I promise that when you catch me trotting out the same old garbage it's more likely to be senility than subterfuge.

So, what's caught my eye recently? I'll avoid any gags about fuelling the old Landrover on unsold reheated pasties during the perceived fuel crisis. You've probably got your own stories. Best one I heard was when Joe pulled up behind someone at a filling station locally, who was carefully topping up four one-gallon cans and two jerry cans. He assured Joe, when asked if he was panic buying, that the tankers were going on strike and there'd be no fuel next week – and that the sky was falling. And if we all acted like you pal, that was undoubtedly going to be the case.

Being out on the road all day Thursday myself, I noticed numerous queues nearly out into the carriageway. Passing one of these (A38 South Brent) I noticed three – yes *three* – bulk tankers in plain view, going about their normal business. I was westbound, and eventually found myself with my fuel gauge in the red wringing the last drips out of a BP diesel pump on the far side of Truro.

I was using the last pump on the forecourt without the 'out of service' label clipped on, and was decidedly glad to have found it when I did. I might've had to borrow some 'cherry-ade' from a friendly Cornishman to get home else.

SUMMER 2012

Sculptors make summer plans

On top of all the rain and miserableness, this year has seen the usual rush of 'preparing for summer' orders in the sawmill.. One of the trends we've watched over the years is the sculptors pushing to get their stuff ready for exhibitions through the balmy months.

Early starters are those actually sculpting in wood. Obviously, they needed to have got a wiggle on earlier, to let the old creative juices flow in time. These have included our old pal Reece, who is wont to carve full-size – if somewhat stylised – sheep in oak or chestnut. He had several (a flockette) to prepare for some sporting fixture to be held in London in July, but I don't think he got tickets to the Men's 100m finals. (But it's good to know some of the money thrown into that particular black hole found its way back to the Southwest after all.) Then a moderately barking Yank had us render down the biggest log of brown burry oak we'd been harbouring, to produce a gurt block he was to shape into a commission for someone with more money than you or I. That went to London as well. These guys are different from the hobbyist sculptors, who chisel away at billets of lime wood throughout the year. They're generally aiming for a swooping eagle, but mostly ending with a big pile of shavings and a crouching wren. Grinling Gibbons is their hero, who carved all manner of stunning stuff in lime around the 1680s.

Others still use the natural shape and grain of the wood to lead their eye, producing beautiful abstract creations at both the 'bit of fun' level, and the more professional 'give 'em a bit of blarney and charge 'em a fortune' level. These are especially useful clients our end, as they can generally find some saleable beauty in the snottiest lump of festering old root plate in the yard. Hence, we love 'em. Unfortunately, these gifted and welcome customers are also of the type to suddenly change direction, and head off into a plexiglass-and-stainless-steel phase (or possibly just up sticks and move to India for a year).

Later in the season come the stone sculptors. They are a different set altogether. Generally coated lightly all over in rock dust, they arrive in the most battered and abused pick-ups you could imagine – and I know your imagination is pretty good in this respect, but they have a bit of a head start. See, they have to drop bliddy great lumps of sandstone/limestone – or Italian marble if they're having a good year – into their trucks. You and I are generally only dropping a few bales of straw in ours, or perhaps some firewood, which tends to bash 'em about rather less. Mind, I did see a couple of blocks on the road backalong which would've sorted the men from the boys. While rolling along the A75 in Dumfries – on a bull-shopping expedition – I passed a low-loader artic rumbling west fully laden with just two irregular blocks of sandstone. My goodness but they were big pebbles.

Back to our local stone sculptors. They visit me not to buy stone – I do sell a bit of granite, but it's a bit hard on the chisels see – but to purchase blocks of green oak as plinths for their work. Sizes range in proportion to the *objet d'art* needing support, going up to cubes 30 inches in each direction. Least favourite was one man's preference for truncated pyramid-shaped plinths. Luckily, I think we've weaned him off them, as they were doing Barrie's head in. (Before you scoff, you try cutting a block 22 inches square one end, tapering to 16 inches square over a length of 4 feet. Then cross-cut the ends, so it'll sit perpendicular top and bottom. It'll do your head in as well.)

Both oak blocks and carvings have to be ready for transportation to arty-farty exhibitions, to be spaced carefully around the grounds of some grand country house – we often get invites, although the whole gig is a bit over my head.

I believe the 'work' is then catalogued for guests and visitors, priced separately with or without the wooden base. Rather embarrassingly, one skilled artisan – and his work is indeed exquisite – has had to admit that certain moneyed but uncultured individuals have started asking him if they can have the plinth but leave the sculpture. Unfortunately, he's a lovely chap with nothing of the cut-throat in his nature, so these requests merely annoy him – it must be a bit like going to Leonardo and asking to buy the frame from round that picture wot he done of that bird smiling. I, however, have less artistic leanings, and see a golden opportunity. I've told him to put on a mark-up, and price the plinths for a straight sale. We'll keep cutting them, and he can set down his chisels and put his feet up!

Pedigree Sherberton Dartmoor ponies in the Swincombe Valley

Surly balers in the rain

For my bucolic chums, I can briefly report that, as well as clipping the last of the Scotties, we snatched another 30 acres of grass, pushing it through the baler with no rubber-band mishaps before the weather broke. With some heavy investment in plastic it's all saved well, although it's got very little nose. The tally to date reads over 900. For good measure, and having no aftergrass, I managed to get some store lambs sorted out and sold.

I suppose urban readers might need further explanation.

With the calendar marching worryingly on, we managed to gather the remaining group of hill ewes dry, and get them sheared. At the same time, we also cut another four fields of grass. With such a short window of opportunity, we couldn't get it dry enough to call it hay, so it needed shrink-wrapping to stop it going mouldy or catching fire. Luckily, it fluffed up enough to go bale reasonably. You see the baler I use works really really well in perfect conditions, when the sun blazes down on crops golden and crispy. Then it'll make very solid bales as fast as you can charge up the row. In damper conditions, however – like its owner – it becomes surly and uncooperative. The faster you try and go in leafy dank stuff, the more you risk it choking on too big a mouthful, or twanging its mechanical knicker elastic.

The former problem can be resolved by shutting off the power, getting down on the floor, and pulling great armfuls of grass back out. Sadly there is no harvesting equivalent to the Heimlich manoeuvre, and you simply have to clear the blessed thing manually. The latter problem, when one of its six 33-foot-long rubber belts breaks, isn't a car crash as long as you've got a spare ready – I keep one tied to the front of the baler. Then, a 15-minute wrestle with these writhing uncooperative snakes will see the baler back into work – and when the weather is on the change, and the crop fit, such matters tend to focus your mind. The lack of a spare will spoil your day. The trick to steady progress is to keep the speed down in the first instance, and watch like a hawk for suspect clumps which might be a problem. This also keeps your mind closely focussed, pretty much to the exclusion of all else.

There are alternatives, of course. There are round balers which will work in wetter conditions, but they bring their own issues. Not least is that their output has to be wrapped immediately, or it sags into misshapen dumplings which jump off the wrapper in an alarming fashion. And anyway, if the grass is too wet, the bales will turn out to be that stinky stuff that gets you plenty of space at the bar of The Strangled Ferret next winter.

Or I could try and make clamp silage – mass heaps in dedicated storage bunkers – which is the norm with proper grown-up farmers. Unfortunately, this not only lacks the convenience of individual bales, but is likely to involve contractors who display an understandable lack of enthusiasm when they hear about two-acre fields sporting outcrops of granite. They then guffaw out loud when they discover there are eight-foot-wide bridges between me and the outside world. Big square balers fall in the same category. Ha! Even my own little old square baler, which hardly ever sees action for the lack of settled weather, has to be hoisted over the parapets dangling from the telehandler in a very undignified fashion.

This season's lack of usable dry spells has drawn all of these options to the top of my mind. This last batch of bales, and the remaining 70 acres uncut, is already several notches below best quality. However well we get it baled now, it won't have that fragrant midsummer waft the cows and I love. At least they're not as fussy as some. One dairy farmer noted recently that, with the quality of the silage he was saving, the rocketing price of concentrates, and low milk prices, he now doesn't have any chance of making any profit in the coming year. Think about that.

Because we are so behind on weather-dependent work, and have very little aftergrass to wean the lambs onto, I've started shipping out the store lamb crop wholesale. An underlying fear is that a sudden dry week might clash with the next sheep fair, or various other stock work and commitments. I didn't want to be still doing July's work late into September again, but that's the way things are heading.

At least the on-going monsoon has led to a flush of grass in otherwise very dry parishes. I noticed one pen of my lambs has gone to a pal who is normally farming in a cloud of dust by this end of the summer. This year he's looking for lambs.

You see, there is a proverbial silver lining in there somewhere. Now, where's me sou'wester?

Johnny Nitram

Every day our poor postie struggles under the substantial weight of predictable bills, infrequent inbound cheques, the newspaper, and an inevitable great sheaf of junk mail. Some of this latter garbage is gaudy free pamphlets exhorting me to shop at one grocer or another, some is unaddressed envelopes suggesting I'd like to give up my hard-earned coin of the realm for some charitable body I haven't heard of. Some, though, is directly addressed to me, also invariably imploring me to part with my coin. It may beg me to buy a particular cattle wormer, a subscription to the *Turkey*

Inseminator's Digest magazine, or hire the services of some glossy legal firm – and by golly, doesn't that firm spend some money on junk mailing me (this last category can often be 'filed' without opening, its contents revealed by the additional info on the outside, but some has to be opened, just in case).

One such this morning was a somewhat heavy – and unsolicited – letter addressed to me, quoting the sawmill business title, from someone called 'The Performing Rights Society'. Curiosity got the better of me, despite it manifestly not being an order for some T&G oak flooring or a beam, so I read on.

They are very anxious, I discovered, that we might be playing music at our place of work for the enjoyment of the staff, while not paying any kind of royalty on this music. This is, they tell me, a heinous crime, and would we like to send them some money, which they'll kindly redistribute to the appropriate musicians?

In my defence, I should point out that I'm all for artists receiving their due credit – and indeed, get very shirty when my own writing is reproduced for profit without my say so. I don't buy knock-off gear, and discourage the kids from dodgy downloads, and am generally full of rectitude and moral fibre. In fact, I seem to recall that the wife has spent some of the meagre egg money I allow her towards allowing the kids to legally download music from the web. On a broader scale, I rather imagine this is like trying to hold back the tide, but we do try. However, I am disinclined to acquiescence to this request. My only knowledge of such payments is when a musically inclined pal sampled some 70- to 80-year-old recordings of Siberian native folk songs on one of his CDs he personally sought out the tribe in question, and sent them a drink.

It does all raise some technical questions, though. Should we listen to the radio at work, would that require a licence? I certainly don't recall Terry Wogan ever telling me not to allow employees to listen for free. If stockman Joe and I are driving in the Landrover, or stopped for a cuppa, with the wireless on, must I instruct him to put some cheese in his ears in case he hears an Abba tune without paying any dues? Oh dearie me, what a minefield.

Happily, the letter was clearly addressed to the sawmill, and it may or may not occur to the PRS that the 'disembowelled cat' howl of the bandsaws, or the high-pitched whine of a pair of duelling Husqavarnas, doesn't leave much room, aurally, for music to play. In fact, everyone wears high-spec ear defenders, so yon music would have to be turned up so loud that the PRS would hear it from their place anyway.

If we're really going to be pedantic – and the matter may be pursued through the courts yet – Barrie does admit to whistling while he runs his mill. I pressed him on this, and he promises me that he sticks to 'out of copyright' tunes. We understand there is some 50-year rule – or is it 70 years after Sir Cliff got near the milestone? – so a spot of Mozart should be safe. Despite taking gainful employment amongst the great unwashed, I suspect Barrie may be a bit cultured on the quiet.

Further proceedings could arise when it comes out that I sing a bit myself. I'm wont to croon to my cows a touch as we meander together over windswept tors. And sometimes while stood at the saw which I run – bored rigid pointing another batch of tree stakes – I might warble a merry tune. Some of these might be the unrecorded hits of 'Johnny Nitram and the Slurry Spreaders', but 'Johnny' passed on some years ago without ever signing a record deal (or, to the best of my knowledge, picking up an instrument) – his tunes were passed on through that cultural medium of the late-night inebriated singalong. He was certainly below the PRS radar.

In either case, my singing is such that the world at large, if it could only hear me, would likely pay me good money to desist. I'm unsure though… is this likely to lead to litigation?

Now, where was that legal firm's latest glossy?

Highlight of my social calendar

One of the highlights of my modest social calendar was complicated this year, as I was partly hosting the two-day Riggit Galloway Cattle Society summer jamboree. Usually we take the kids on a week's holiday, to coincide with this bash. We head to the relevant spot in the UK, taking a log cabin/ holiday cottage for the duration. This means the kids get to drag us along to four or five days of jollies with them, but have to tolerate Daddy sloping

off to talk cows for a couple of days. Apparently this isn't what holidaying Daddies are supposed to do, although it was several years before they cottoned on to the fact that their school chums' holidays were different. Ours often seemed to take place in rain-lashed upland districts, where such hirsute cattle, and their breeders, might be found roaming the hill. I think Northumberland, Kirkcudbright and the North York Moors are eminently suitable holiday locations, but the little beggars are wise to this now, and suggesting that more high wires, sunny beaches and theme parks ought to feature. I'm fighting a rearguard action, pleading that the Auchtercraggy Porridge Museum is a real treat, and that Cumbrian Nasal Pipe recital was an evening to be treasured.

The author on his hols in the Lake District

Still, while the Riggit beano is usually to be found up north, this year several members had requested a trip to kinder climes, so the assembly took place in the West Country, so the small Coakers had to tolerate a 'staycation'. Plans included a day spent on Exmoor visiting some very good farming folk, who subsequently filled us with scones and cream, followed by a BBQ down the Exe Valley – Riggit burgers – and then a day's cultural outings and yet more nosh on Dartmoor.

The assembled visitors to these events are an eclectic mix of smallholders, commercial upland cattlemen and conservation graziers, with a smattering of folk who just like interestingly hairy bullocks. The accents rolling around the table this summer ranged from deep West Country dialects to rich rural Cumbrian and Northumbrian brogues, although nobody made it down from north of the border – I think the floods around Carlisle scared them off. One Northumbrian admitted, as he was being guided to his Dartmoor hotel late in the evening, through rising floodwaters and howling gales, that he thought he was falling off the edge of the world. It is very much the case that all Northern and Scottish farmers assume us Nancy Southerners live in such favoured climes that we don't know what weather really is. Well, we firmly disabused them of that this year, although being of a hardy nature the driving rain and wind merely added to the sense of achievement. When the Northumbrian drove into my yard the following morning, he pulled up, lowered the window on his huge Land Cruiser and announced in an accent a bit softer than the *Auf Wiedersehen, Pet* lads: 'Aahm lookin' fer a fella the name of Noah?'

There is in fact yet another category of delegates in the group. One or two, when pressed, admit little interest in the cattle themselves, but have got wind of what a fun time we collectively have. You see, as well as having to look at/talk about cattle occasionally, most of the time we tour various majestic rolling landscapes, in between halting to sample the rich array of victuals and refreshments to be found. The calibre of some of the good old boys who've had a lifetime of wrestling large beasts and weathering the storms leads to some very salubrious evenings. At last year's shindig on the North York Moors, after another evening eating as much as was humanly possible, a posse of very high-mileage characters sat around the top of the table, chairs pushed back to reflect on life. I sat my boy at the other end of the table, and told him to keep quiet and enjoy, and sure enough it was better than aught on t'telly.

I do hope I kept up the standard hosting my part of the beano. Admittedly, one group of Dartmoor cows didn't want to be viewed, and spent 30 minutes pawing the ground snorting, stood in front of their calves for all the world like a bunch of musk ox facing down a wolf pack. Their owner warned us that the noisy ones weren't the problem. The quiet one in the centre was the one to watch – a bit like the velociraptor in *Jurassic Park*. My own ladies, meanwhile, are trained to the bag, and are a rather different kettle of fish. As the clouds cleared, they gallumphed down to us when I called, slobbering all over me and nosing right up to our very impressed visitors.

It was all highly enjoyable, but you'll have to excuse me now. I've got to go and wring out some grass for the baler.

Memorial slab

As I told you backalong, that dodgy bucolic mongrel Egbert notices that some of the cottages in his local hamlet change hands so quickly now that he no longer bothers to catch the owners' names. This reached new levels recently when he noticed a fresh 'For Sale' sign outside one such desirable country residence – 'magnificent moorland views, delightfully isolated community'. The estate agents' placard is proudly stuck in the roadside bank, not 30 feet from where the previous sign – from when the house last changed hands – is clearly visible, thrown into a gorse bush. We don't know what they expect in these places, but they sure ain't finding it.

He went on to tell me about a recent community effort, attempting to bring together residents in this isolated hamlet. It started when one worthy local – his chum the Brigadier – thought it would be fitting to erect a commemorative stone, marking the Diamond Jubilee of HM The Queen. So the gentleman of the piece set things in motion. First he prevailed upon a couple of the dishevelled peasants nearby – none other than Egbert and Farmer 'X' – to find a suitable stone, and organise relocating it to the village green. He, meanwhile, would go off and persuade some of the villagers to put their hands in their pockets and help fund an inscription.

Now while the Brigadier found the milk of human kindness was a little backward in coming forward, and was soon embroiled in disagreements about the exact wording of the inscription, at least the stone-hunting party quickly put their hands upon an impressively large slab. In a gap between silaging, Farmer X oversaw operations as one of Egbert's drivers scooped the slab up with a large telehandler. (Egbert has a motley collection of helpmates. We think he pays them in filleted roadkill and all the scrumpy they can drink.)

This rock, it turned out, must've been all of four tonnes because the machine could hardly get it clear of the deck. Somehow, Egbert's man – 'The Rock Pixie' as the Brigadier subsequently named him – bullied it the half mile up the road without gouging out too much tarmac, and flopped it down opposite the pub. Soon thereafter, a stonemason lad turned up and chiselled the inscription, and there it now lies.

There is, however, a little more to the tale as I understand things. A coda if you will, relevant only to selected folk.

What Egbert and 'X' neglected to tell anyone – mostly because not everyone would grasp the significance – was that the massive slab of granite was dug from the 'crossroads' field in 2001, where most of the livestock that had grazed the valley was piled up high, and fired.

They'd agreed between themselves that this commemorative stone marking the Diamond Jubilee – of the monarch they both hold extremely dear – might as well be discreetly serving a second purpose. The fact that its significance is invisible to almost everyone else probably reflects how the more recent inhabitants regard the maelstrom that hit the community in 2001.

Meanwhile, I've been trying to put some thoughts together about this past 'summer'. I suspect that I'll have put the baler to bed by the time you get this, and maybe even a week or two earlier than last year, but hell's teeth it's been a struggle again, hasn't it?

One of the moments of clarity that occurred, as I was coaxing more of my soggy lank grass off the deck, was this here organic business. I haven't heard detail yet, but given how 'conventional' farmers have struggled with disease control in their corn crops this year, I can only guess what organic crops will be like. Now I am given to understand that it has been DEFRA policy to encourage us to go organic in recent years. Extra subsidies and the like – and please stop shouting at me, I don't care much one way or the other – to stop using those nasty fungicide sprays and so on. And so who carries the can for all that black mouldy garbage that is no doubt lying in some grain bins now? Will they have to eat it? Now Google 'Ergot' and come back to me on this.

I would have thought that someone should 'fess up', and admit that the policy could be proved a phenomenal folly this summer.

And while we're on this line of thought, I've a little snippet I picked up recently. While I don't know much about GMOs, other than a cynic's suspicion that any chemical company developing them must surely be doing so only with an eye to selling you ever more spray, there are other bodies working on GMOs. One such, in India, has cooked up a potato which is yielding 15–20% higher yields with no extra inputs. That's the kind of number that'd make you sit up and notice, isn't it?

If they could now develop a perennial starch food plant – which would eliminate annual tillage – then we'd be cooking with gas. Better still would be if it could thrive on wet acid soils, meaning I might look at something other than grumpy Blackfaced ewes.

Let me know when it comes along.

The Grange
Much Cussing
17 August 2012

Dear Mr Heckling

I write in the vain hope that my family and I might get some kind of apology for the unfortunate events of Sunday last, which have quite ruined our introduction to village life.

I understand that, when moving into a country parish such as this, one must expect to encounter certain quaint customs. Indeed, since Rupert's decision to downsize from his job in the City, we have been looking forward to getting 'involved'. I myself was thinking to join the local WI, perhaps serving on the Parish Council, or the committee of the Pony Club. Rupert had fully meant to further his interests in fly fishing and try a spot of pheasant shooting and the like. So when you and your brother invited us to the fête in your front meadow, we were delighted. To be involved so soon after arriving was a real treat... or so we thought.

It was mere coincidence that our youngest, Veronica, was down from her digs at uni that weekend. As you will see, we are beginning to regret this. I would go as far, in fact, as to say we are asking ourselves if the country life is really for us.

I feel that not telling us in advance about the theme of the main attraction, (and I refer of course to the 'Middle White sow most like her owner' contest), or the astonishing amount of drunken ribaldry that accompanied it, was a cruel and possibly deliberate omission.

As you well know, on arrival Rupert parked the Bentley where instructed by a friendly chuckling young man. In hindsight, this in itself should have raised our suspicions, as no one else was directed to park at that end of the meadow, and I thought I heard him greet us with something about 'heffin DFLs in convertibles'. Although I discounted it at the time, I have come to learn that this youth is your nephew, and that 'DFL' is apparently a derogatory term for someone recently relocated from London.

Before the main event, we allowed ourselves to be sat on a straw bale and treated to some of the local hospitality. Rupert sampled what he was assured was very weak cider, while Veronica and myself partook of something jocularly called 'Egbert's clover mead'. I didn't see the bottles, or approved labels, as all the drinks seemed to be poured freehand from earthenware jugs and one-gallon plastic bottles. I have a suspicion that some of what we were offered might have been home-made.

Anyway, as the afternoon wore on, Rupert said he felt somewhat under the weather, and left us to rest in the shade of the willow tree beside your pond. We both know quite well what happened to Veronica next.

I had erroneously assumed that livestock exhibitions were attended by pampered and primped pedigree animals, carefully prepared over many weeks, and that their handlers were expert professionals. I had little understanding that strangers could be awarded some kind of wildcard entry, although Veronica was initially flattered to be so invited to participate.

By the time I realised that the true nature of the competition was to assess the similarity of handler to pig, it was too late, and entrants were parading around the roped-off enclosure. Something else that only then became clear was that the pig poor Veronica had been given to exhibit was not sufficiently tamed. While many of the assembly seemed to find the resulting spectacle amusing - hilarious even - I was mortified. I'll have you know that that frock was from Milan, and cost several hundred pounds. I suggest that my daughter took the upset so well speaks highly of her breeding and upbringing, although the frock is now ruined. The stains were one thing, but when the straps became torn, I could see what was sure to happen. Unfortunately, it was about then that my legs seem to have gone into some kind of temporary spasm, and I found myself unable to stand - the affable Egbert had been around with his earthenware jug on several occasions. (His repeated assurances that the mead was hardly alcoholic at all might've been, well frankly, a lie.) I thought it was a kind gesture, if a little improper, on the part of your nephew to help Veronica back into the remains of her frock, although I don't see why so many of the villagers thought this even funnier, or why they started whistling and hooting so. Is this some kind of backward rural tradition?

I must admit that about then I was overcome with drowsiness, and may have briefly closed my eyes. I believe it was then that another competition started - called, I am lately told - the 'Gurt dung fling'. How our Bentley came to be parked alone in what could only be described as the fallout zone is unclear, although once more your nephew's behaviour comes to mind.

When Rupert finally returned from his rest under the willow tree, he informed me he didn't feel able to drive, and insisted we walk home. Hence we remained unaware of what had been landing on, and in, the car. Rupert only discovered the mess the following day. The dealership say the leather is quite ruined, and the paint seems to be bubbling slightly as well. Rupert is talking to our insurers, who have asked for your contact details.

We couldn't seem to find Veronica when we came to leave at dusk that evening. It was much later in the night when she finally returned, and happily didn't seem to be any the worse for wear. In fact, she seemed to be in perfectly good health, the fresh country air putting some colour in her cheeks I thought. (I might say her health is in question now though, as she has been quite unwell on several mornings since the above events. I'm not altogether sure why.)

Yours sincerely

Tabitha Ponsonby-Smythe

AUTUMN 2012

My inner Luddite

I know it's a big disappointment to some of you, but technology and I are never going to be best buddies. I am prepared to adopt new gadgets (generally several years behind events, and then only grudgingly). Obviously, my weapons-grade tightfistedness has nothing to do with this, nor my innate mistrust of anyone trying to sell me something I hadn't thought to ask for. It must be the inner Luddite speaking.

Why this very book, hammered out on the farm's computer, is reluctantly written on some irritating bit of software that nice Bill Gates chap commissioned. In itself, I'm sure it's fantastic. I don't know how the tiny goblins frantically working in the computer manage, but they seem to be able to conjure up the nonsense I tappity-tap onto the keyboard, scrolling it down across the screen for me. Well done Bill. My problem is that once you'd tamed 'em and got them doing these tricks, you couldn't leave them to it – could you?

For some reason, this software stuff has to be updated (and while Alison has explained the whys to me, I forget... surely it can't be a 'built-in obsolescence'? Surely Bill has made enough money now?). But, with each upgrade, the tiny little goblins seem to have developed either new tricks, or possibly bad habits. They suddenly get it in their little heads that I want bullet points, bigger spacing, or a different page layout when I come to write anything. This is a bit like dropping your favourite coffee mug. As the pieces are spinning away from the impact, you know full well that the coffee in the replacement might be exactly the same, but somehow it's not the same.

I suppose I must be the marketing department's worst enemy. I might be quite happy to part with piles of my meagre coin for good gear initially, which is great for everybody as far as it goes, but I am then quite happy to run that gear forever. Worse, I never... and I really mean never... replace something merely because the latest model has some 'go faster stripe' and an improved cup holder.

In fact, I'll deliberately run an old bit of gear into the ground if I suspect its replacement will have some stupid 'change for the sake of change' about it. Even worse, if I can drag something out of a skip, give it a lick of paint and a new winding spring, and it does what I want of it, I will, and then use it until the cows come home.

So the latest smart-phone technology is a dark art to me. I do have a mobile device, which I carry when I'm away from home and need Alison to have some way of nailing me down. No one has the number – and you certainly won't be getting it, chum – and I believe it has a torch function beyond its ability to make and take calls, although I've never used it.

And I know very well that some of you aren't racing much ahead of me…

With this in mind, I was tickled to sit around a table with some of my bucolic chums the other night, needing to find a way of taking photos while far out on the veldt. These pics then needed to be transmitted to another one of our number. Now she is probably the handiest of the bunch assembled, when it comes to this kind of thing, and suggested they could email the pics they'd taken using their mobile phones. This raised varying grades of confused looks. So she suggested bringing their phones along next time we were to meet, and she'd use something called Bluetooth to transfer the photos. (I understood all of the actual individual words used, but put together they made gobbledegook sentences as far as I was concerned.) 'Ah!' said one or two of the farmers present, 'that's a capital plan.' Others needed this phenomenon explaining, but soon seemed to have a handle on how this trick might be accomplished.

'Beggar me!' said I, as the conversation moved on. 'You can take pictures with a mobile phone?'

Mansion tax

Forgive me, for I am perplexed.

See, a group of very 'middle of the road' politicians keep banging on about something called the 'mansion tax'. Details are scant, but then they need to be. From the news headlines I'm unclear whether this tax would be a one-off, or every decade? Or every year? Would the tax apply only if the property were actually paid outright… what if there was still a mortgage? If it's a rented property, then who pays this tax? Will the magic £1 (or £2) million threshold be raised in line with inflation? Would a drop in house prices cause rebates? Will a gurt big house split into separate living accommodation for, say, different generations still qualify? Remember, if they were minded to pursue the matter, the Treasury would hardly hold up the marginal cases: they'd point out the migrant Russian oligarchs and Premier Division footballers. They're not going to use the example of an elderly widow living in an ordinary house with a large garden which happens to lie exactly where the land-gobbling supermarket wants to build its new superstore, making the house worth XYZ.

And then will a couple hundred acres of rich farmland tip the attached ag tie bungalow from the fifties over the threshold? What if the poor beggar on it is milking a cows at a cash loss… is he still to be taxed as a squillionaire, because of the value of the soil under his feet?

In fact, with a favourable wind (and by getting rid of that god-awful sitting tenant) Château Coaker might very well qualify.

Oh – but how the questions stack up. We'd better explore some basics. The childish idea that 'rich people have got lots of money, so they should give it to poor people' got a rather extensive airing through the last century. Many countries took the concept to its logical conclusion, and levelled the playing field by force. Subsequently, whole generations became institutionalised to the point that, when someone finally left the proverbial door open, their social structures were so rubbish that said oligarchs simply walked up and stole whole chunks of these nation's assets.

And here in the UK don't we already have a thing called 'income tax', where the more you earn, the higher rate of tax you pay? And please stop bleating about how 'the rich always dodge income tax' – that's a matter of enforcement. And remember, the moment any mansion tax was announced, several gaping loopholes would be found by cute accountants. It's an unavoidable reality that people who gather vast fortunes are either very smart, or will employ accountants to be smart on their behalf. That's human nature.

On top of income tax, stamp duty already places higher taxation on expensive homes, and council tax bands are set by the value of your house. So apart from having to pay extra tax to earn this wealth, it already costs more to then spend it. And saying this mansion is so valuable is OK, but if you sell it and it's gone up in value... why! Here's the taxman again, this time with his 'capital gains tax'. Even when you die – unless you've long since given it all away – HM Government grabs nearly half the loot with yet another tax.

Being rich, and living in a big house, costs rather more than it seems.

And although there isn't sufficient space to unravel it here, I expect if you wanted to look it could be that with the gardeners, cleaners, nannies and the like, the row of plush houses out by the golf club, or with access to moorings on the estuary, probably employ a significant percentage of the local population. Certainly sales of my oak beams, and Galloway hide rugs and beef, help recycle money from some of those households back to a poor-ass tenant farmer. I occasionally see a Coutts cheque.

Because their actions and activities affect everyone, kicking the wealthy doesn't necessarily have the effect you might desire.

Which leads us onto where industrious 'go-getters' fit in our society. If they can't reap the rewards of their efforts (and by saying they should be taxed ever higher on their spoils, that's where you're heading) why would they bother? They will do one of two things: decamp for somewhere hot and sunny, possibly where their efforts are appreciated, or worse, they simply won't bother. What drives a country's industry, if not them?

Pretending that because someone lives in a big house they've got more than they deserve is an ignorant viewpoint. It's fuelled by jealousy and idleness – or the wish to grab cheap votes off stupid people. It's also a dangerous concept to promote, fuelling the selfish idea that everyone should share in the rewards of other's efforts. History shows that's not how economies are built: it is how they are destroyed.

Waggly Briggins

A couple of the kids scrawling about my feet were very excited last weekend about some bicycle race that was coming through. I'd heard rumblings about it from my lovely little wife, who does Parish Councillor type activities* on occasion, so I was vaguely aware that it was forthcoming.

Apparently the road was to be closed. We don't know what would've happened if this had clashed with my needing to get hay home before the rain, or if I'd arrived at a road crossing with a herd of cows. I sometimes drive a flock of sheep a couple of miles along this road, avoiding a river they can't cross. Many of my colleagues would recognise the purple-faced outrage that greets us when doing this, from about every fourth car driver. I generally smile and wave to everyone I've held up (although it wears a bit thin when some rep nudges right up to my ankles, or looks like he's going to run over Gyp). Sharp words have been used, and on more than one occasion drivers have suddenly been moved to pull back and lock their doors. A pal similarly burdened with moorland road crossings is a heavily built man, with an ordinarily mellow demeanour. However, drivers who expect him to levitate his stock across the road find themselves in the mire of his dark side when they try to nudge him or his cattle aside, or tootle their horn. I understand that the new tactic involves a hefty swipe with his hazel stick – read cudgel – which seems to make them back off.

It is hardly a new phenomenon. When I was a spotty stripling, my Dad and I were moving the predecessors of the same flock along the road one spring. While I hunted a couple of miscreants out of the woods on the higher side, some berk thought he'd just push past this silly old bloke on his bay mare. Ha! Was he in for a surprise! The old man had a big voice when riled, and from my vantage point within the young spruce plantation I could soon hear the one side of the 'discussion'. It was quickly apparent that someone 'had better get out of his car and take his jacket off if he felt like that'. With a sinking heart I pushed my strays back down to the wall, knowing full well Dad's ticker was fast on its way out, afloat on a raft of health issues. Roadside fisticuffs were certainly not just what the doctor had ordered.

By the time I'd reappeared from the undergrowth, the driver of the nearest car had, in a stance I've come to recognise, wound his windows up, locked his doors and pulled right back. As I took up my position beside the old man, and we continued along behind the flock, he asked *sotto voce* what the driver was doing. I told him, and he whispered that this was just as well, as if it had gone any further, I was going to have to thump the bloke for him. Thanks Dad.

And so I'm curious to note what happens nowadays, should an actual road closure unknowingly coincide with my agrarian doings. Happily, it wasn't tested on this occasion.

For some reason it turned out that the kids weren't the only ones excited about seeing this bloke Waggly Briggins pedal through, with the hillside verges packed. It was just like the morning of that solar eclipse – there must've been thousands of 'em. Well, I thought, this bicycle race must be a lot more exciting than I'd assumed.

We'd arrived with a few minutes to spare, so I was able to stand about in the sun and chat with a few locals, but quickly dozens of motorcycle outriders started streaming past, leapfrogging each other as they stopped along the way. They were mostly coppers – from all over the country we ascertained – along with medics and stewards. Before the racers appeared we'd already seen three of these motorcycle outriders very nearly pile up; and then the cavalcade arrived. Seemingly, this race involves a few lads pedalling their hearts out, while three times as many hangers-on charge along behind them in the shape of support cars, media vehicles, and dozens more motorcycle outriders. They jostled for position, with flashing lights and blaring horns,

swerving all over the road, and generally acted like they were in a banger race. Fascinating. One or two straggling cyclists got in amongst the cars, and I suppose that the rules allow for their removal from the race by... well... 'Sudden Death'.

I must admit that it was quite a spectacle, but I'm sure I could've made it a lot more interesting with a trailer load of bales, or 50 meandering bullocks.

From what I hear, the Parish Council mostly row about who is prepared to pay for the upkeep of the one public loo in the parish. The answer apparently is no one, and hence we're about to take a small step back from civilisation.

The author in training for next year's Tour de France

Internal memo, recipient's eyes only
Department of Revenues and Taxation
Ref 21/774/2012   3-3-2013

To: Mr Grimesworth
From: Dunstan LeMonbiter

SUBJECT Horace Buttercup
I have reviewed your report, detailing this lengthy, and may I say costly, investigation. Obviously the whole affair is extremely sensitive, given the media's interest in the Chancellor's push to 'tax the wealthy', and there are some points I wish to clarify.

I am led to believe that the reasons for selecting the target for this operation, one Horace Buttercup, remain unclear. I have heard suggestion that your line manager, one Ms Blizzen, lives locally to the target, and that an incident involving her rambling club and Mr Buttercup's dogs may have some bearing on the matter.

Nonetheless, I accept that you were acting under instruction, and your preliminary investigation into the tax returns, acquisitions and land holdings of Mr Buttercup were evidence enough to trigger further enquiries. Obviously, the knowledge that he annually receives something over £200,000 in European subsidies, but declared last year a net income of a mere £6400, is in itself suspicious.

In your report, you have clearly stated that Mr Buttercup has land assets currently valued at something over £3 million, and appears to have tractors and harvesters and the like conservatively valued at £0.5 million. His principal residence is currently, according to the local Council Tax banding, valued at between £100,00 and £125,000, but since you indicate that it – Combe Hollow Manor – is actually a seven-bedroom Elizabethan mansion, I think we'll assume Mr Buttercup's position as a Councillor might have played in his favour somehow. (Incidentally, I spoke to the offices of 'Borders Heritage' yesterday. Upon hearing Mr Buttercup's name they declared they had 'no knowledge of him or that bloody house', and slammed the phone down.)

I see you confirm that the newly built cottage you found in the lower copse, along with three others behind the yard, do exist. This is despite detailed searches revealing they are listed as two cowsheds, a log store and a kennel. I am further inquisitive to know the truth in rumours you heard that the 'workshops' and 'slurry store' are in fact let out as units to seven local businesses, which would indicate significant rental income which doesn't seem to be accounted for.

The extensive campsite you refer to has already been investigated, but the satellite images of caravans used as evidence were later conclusively proved to be '72 hayricks', so I am afraid that matter, at least, must rest.

The subject of Mr Buttercup's livestock has also caught my eye. You see, since records show he only has three Angora goats and a yak, and you've raised suspicions that he actually maintains a significant herd of pedigree cattle, I have looked further. Were you aware that a man of the same name lifted the top price (£37k) in the Glen McSporran spring sales this year? Or that the animal 'Combe Hollow Emperor' was champion beast at several major agricultural shows last summer? I note from the sale catalogue McSporran Marts kindly forwarded that the vendor has collected several thousand 'straws' of semen – if you ever – and has them for sale at £50 each.

Perhaps you might've enquired closer here.

The subject's consistent denial that he keeps sheep is subject to other investigations, as his name appears as a regular purchaser of something called 'mule gimmers' at an annual sale somewhere in Cumbria. Sadly, as he pays in cash, and gives a false address, the trail has gone cold. Our colleagues in DEFRA admit that the electronic tags from last autumn's consignment were eventually located in a rabbit warren beside a service station on the southbound M6. They suspect Buttercup is maintaining something they refer to as a 'flying flock' of several hundred, and must therefore be producing something over a thousand lambs per season for which no records appear, but would be worth some tens of thousands of pounds.

Didn't you notice evidence of this?

You observed that several men were gainfully employed feeding a large number of what you call 'ornamental fowl', in the farm's woods. Hadn't it occurred that these might've been pheasants, and therefore there might be some kind of organised 'shoot' through the winter months? You do realise that these shoots can generate significant sums, and are frequently used as gratuities within select circles? The least enquiries uncover that gundogs from the Combe Hollow kennel are advertised in the shooting press for upwards of £1200 each. The advert quotes a mobile number, advising that one ask for 'Horace'. You don't suppose there's a connection, do you?

Regarding your reference to some horses which Mr Buttercup has exercised on the ridge above the farmstead. While I'm sure that some may indeed be retired, and need to be kept fit as is claimed, had you by any chance noticed the winner of last May's Golden Platter at Shapley Downs? The horse was named 'Combe Blaster', owned and trained by none other than one 'H. Buttercup'. The trophy, my assistant has uncovered, comes with a substantial cash prize, and an unconnected investigation into betting irregularities has revealed significant wagers centred on

this animal's placing at Shapley Downs. The horse subsequently appears, after a reported flurry of very expensive matings, to have been exported some three months later to an undisclosed buyer from the Persian Gulf, at a reputed cost of £2 million.

I really do feel you might've enquired closer.

Sadly, I've to advise you that this investigation is to be suspended. The lack of progress remains an issue, and Buttercup's accountants (Slippit & Dodger) are threatening to tender a substantial bill, quoting some EU directive, for wasted time if we cannot produce hard evidence.

In any case I have been telephoned by Sir Henry. After a lengthy tirade on 'the best bleddy driven birds in the county', he's ordered that I reassign you to Felixstowe container terminal with immediate effect.

Dunstan LeMonbiter

Email   sent 13-5-2013
From: 'warramungapostoffice.com.aus'
To: 'townsvillepolicestation.com.aus'

SUBJECT 'Lost Pom?'
G'day Bob, how's the big city this morning?
We've got a bit of an odd one turned up, mate, and I could do with some advice…

About 10 days ago, one of the road-train drivers dropped a bloke into town he'd found wandering about, a coupla hundred clicks out on the tableland track and obviously in quite a state. This fella had a fairly bad sunburn, severe dehydration, an assortment of sores and spider bites, and was just about barking mad. Well, after the nurse at the clinic had seen to the worst of the sunburn and the sores and what-have-you, we installed him in the hotel, although George is demanding to know who's gonna to foot the bill. As a holding answer I've said that the State will take responsibility if no one else will (although George is sceptical after that backpacker last year).

Anyway, this fella. He was only wearing a tattered pair of strides and a ragged shirt, and had no ID on him, so he's a bit of a mystery. Once he'd calmed down a bit, we tried to get his story out of him, but frankly it's pretty garbled. See, he claims he's some kind of inspector, although I don't think he knows exactly where he is, or where he's from come to that. His name could be Grimesworth, and from his accent I'd say he's a Pom, but it's hard to be sure. His tongue is still swollen due to the spider bite on his cheek, and the nurse says it'll make his speech difficult for some time.

He keeps on ranting about something called 'Eeeooo directives', whatever they are,

and someone called Horace. The hotel Sheila says he also shouts about someone called Buttercup, and 'Felix's toe' in his sleep. Mean anything to you?

Now obviously, there's Ned Buttercup who runs the Wallaby Flats Station out on the tableland, but I don't see how this goanna could've walked all that way. In fact, I got Ned on the radio yesterday and asked if he knew anything about it, and he assured me he didn't. The only Horace he knows of is a farmer cousin back in England, but Ned doesn't think he'd be anything to do with this, being only a simple grazier and all. And Ned's a pretty sound bloke.

Anyway, this fella keeps on about his mission, and shouts about all manner of 'breaches'. He's very confused about the feral donkeys and brumbies he's seen. Well, he calls them 'equines', and goes on about whether they've been microchipped or not. I don't like to tell him there's not nearly as many about now, since we rounded up a coupla thousand for the National Park service last month, and shipped 'em down to that Cape Meat Packers barge.

We thought he was settling down after a few days, but he got very exercised when a mob of camels wondered through town yesterday evening, heading for the creek. Then that night, the carpet python George keeps upstairs in the pub – to keep the mice down – got in his bed, and he's right back to gibberish again I'm afraid.

I think he might've come across some of the Urquhart's stockmen out branding calves and upset them somehow, because one of the sores – the one on his left buttock – bears an uncanny resemblance to the Urquhart's bullock brand, and the nurse says it certainly could be a burn mark. Their team usually hit the pub on the last Friday in the month, so I'll get someone to have a chat with 'em if you like. Funnily enough, old Urquhart is brother-in-law to Ned Buttercup, now I come to think of it. I wonder if there's some kind of connection there.

However, who cut the notches in his right ear remains unknown although, again, the pattern does remind me somewhat of the Wallaby Flats mark. I s'pose I'd better ask them about that as well when I see 'em. The nurse thinks the wound across his backside might be a mulesing scar* if she didn't know better. The last time she saw something similar was when young Thompson got caught with Grundy's daughter a few years back, but as you'll recall, nothing was ever proved.

Anyway, whaddya want us to do with this drongo, mate?

Take care

Harry O'Rourke

Ozzie practice of cutting a strip of skin from under the tail of newborn lambs to prevent wool growing there, to avoid poop sticking and thus attracting flies and maggots

What is a 'farmer'?

I was reading somewhere that the number of farmers has dropped by X, Y or even Z, but the author admitted it was hard to pin down a number, depending on how you counted. Surveys of the numbers of farmers must have some way of finding a figure. This got me thinking: how do you quantify exactly who is a 'farmer'? It's no use using NFU membership as the yardstick, as there's all sorts of people who pay a sub, including corporate members far removed from the view you or I might have in our mind's eye. In fact, there was a famous ex-Prime Minister (our most famous ex-PM) who was a paid-up member, giving his profession as 'farmer' (whilst holding up a two-fingered salute, if you need a clue – although I don't think his Tonyness is likely to turn up at your local livestock committee meeting).

And likewise, it'll be no good using a declaration by anyone that he's a farmer. I can think of property developers, ex-bankers, solicitors and surgeons, along with smugglers and drug dealers, who have claimed, when it suits them, to be 'simple farmers'. One bloke was recently seen locally swearing blind he was such a farmer because he's got some cows, whilst it's well known he's holding multiple directorships with a widely varied business portfolio. And then I bumped into a delightful fellow recently, who breeds 'a few cows', and we talked cattle for a while. Closer enquiries however revealed that he owns, so it appears, half of Scotland. Would it be accurate to regard him as a farmer? (I'd wager he doesn't actually fill the feeders himself, or rely on the price of a few hairy steers for his living, come to that.)

You look around your own parish. How many fellas do you know who're actually reliant on farming, if livelihood is the measure to use? If 'farming' is to live from the primary production of food from the land – oh all right, or the fish hatchery if you're going be pedantic – then does the chap qualify who grazes a few sheep in among the 128 static caravans he rents out in the lower meadow? Or the lad who throws a few round bales to 30 sucklers when he gets back from his main occupation felling trees/driving an HGV/laying blocks? (delete as applicable).

If your Missus takes in a few B&B customers to help with a little pin money, not only might it dislodge you from your favourite spot at the breakfast table, but would it also disqualify you from the strictest description of being a farmer? And I don't care how much that maid pays you for those few bales of hay for her riding 'oss, unless she's using it to shepherd and gather the hill ewes, supplying it isn't farming. Interesting, isn't it?

I certainly wouldn't qualify, if we're using this test. Strip away the writing, sawmilling, beef/hide rug sales, disallow the speaking engagements or Dartmoor pony sales – well, unless I could find a salami factory for them – and I still wouldn't be a farmer. You see, doing 'pink spotted butterfly habitat management', or whatever it is I'm doing, isn't really farming either.

As it goes, if I didn't do all the above, the cows and I would very soon run into real trouble, and I'd soon be even less of a farmer. (If I'm honest, that rather appeals… my problems would suddenly stop being mine, and become one of the bank's.)

I suppose you can use the priorities measure. Do you run the odd diverse enterprise to help support your fondness for milking cows, or is it the other way round? If you stopped doing whatever else it is you do, would you still be 'you'? If I stopped owning sucklers and my motheaten ewes, I can't see that I would be the same person. (Admittedly, some of those close to me suggest there might be a marked improvement if I didn't keep on with it, but what do they know?)

So what is a farmer? In the end, even without the faint whiff of red diesel or sheep grease, or being scrubbed completely clean of mud and cow poop, you can still tell. I think we'd both know one when we met 'em, whatever anyone else might say. And that must be the real test.

Where is farming going?

I don't know if you clocked it, but the news the other day featured a report on the decline in numbers of the UK's nesting birds. The figures quoted were something like 240 million down to 160 million over 40 years. Forgive me if I haven't got it exactly right, but it was the radio news at 'stupid o'clock' when I am not at my sharpest. Still, the gist was that the nice dicky-birds have been disappearing fast and, as usual, the reason given was 'because of the way the land is farmed'.

OK pal, let's take some of this to pieces. First off, let's talk about what else has happened in the last few decades. I seem to recall that the human population has gone UP by a pretty similar percentage over the same period. I have no doubt that the surface area under roads, car parks, houses and supermarkets has likewise skyrocketed. The consequent loss and change of habitat must have a massive impact.

It is also pertinent that urban sprawl is generally outward from existing towns. It is a matter of fact that these have mostly grown in proximity to the best land, and/or river/estuarine trade routes. Before Mr and Mrs Ug came out of their caves, these habitats would've been carrying far higher populations of birdies than, say, some blasted mountaintop. As civilisation developed, so the wildlife has had to move sideways. And then in recent decades there has been the phenomenal growth in both motorcars and aeroplanes. I don't doubt for a moment that pollution from both has had a significant impact.

Likewise all the detritus we produce, turning millions of years' worth of hydrocarbons into plastic carrier bags and packaging. Not that it's relevant to the UK argument, but I understand that there is a corner of the Pacific where a vast pool of tiny plastic shreds is now collecting in a gigantic oceanic eddy. It floats about the ocean's currents for years, eventually getting caught in a watery cul de sac. The local wildlife is, not surprisingly, badly affected. I daresay there will be parallels within the UK ecosystem.

And back to farming. It is undoubtedly true that the seventies saw hedgerows grubbed up in the name of efficiency. It would hardly be otherwise, as we moved from ploughing with horses and oxen, to adopting tractors. It is also true, however, that the last couple of decades have seen this trend firmly reversed. The rationalising has largely been done, and the length of the country there are new hedgerows growing, along with conservation margins, ponds and amenity plantations. Likewise, while modern farming is evermore reliant on chemicals to protect arable crops, the rules regarding their usage are steadily tightening. The most toxic weapons in the arsenal are gradually being banned.

The blind statement that farming is responsible for the decline in dicky-birds is, at the very least, extremely disingenuous. The blame lies with every one of us.

And this in turn brings us onto a bigger question. Quite apart from these specific spurious allegations, shouldn't we ask where farming is going?

An example? You may or may not know about the tense on-going discussions about slug pellets. The authorities are threatening to withdraw approval, as the active ingredient is apparently turning up in watercourses. Now during this dreadful wet year arable farmers have been fighting a rearguard action, initially to protect and harvest the 2012 crops, and subsequently to try and establish next year's, in 'suboptimal' conditions. A major problem has been slugs, which love the wet and, indeed, copious amounts of the little blue pellets have been broadcast. Hence the 'discussions'.

This situation, along with dubious allegations about the causes of declining bird numbers, reveals a wider picture. You can blame farmers for everything if you like. Tie our hands, restrict our operations and keep us under close scrutiny if you will. But shouldn't you be asking what alternatives we have, with so many billions of mouths to feed?

If, sticking with the example, arable farmers hadn't been able to resort to sprinkling slug pellets liberally about the place, the simple truth is that tens of thousands of tonnes of crops would've been spoiled, and vast acreages of next year's would already be in tatters.

Here in the UK, we can – reluctantly – afford the sharp price rises that global shortages bring, but other countries are less fortunate, and people go hungry. Hard choices are upon us.

WINTER 2012/2013

Gyp – still top dog

Gyp-the-Wonder-Dog has a problem – apart, that is, from the balding tip to his tail, or the scabby patch on his head. You see, he's been cock of the walk for some time, and has been enjoying the privileges this canine status brings. His troubles stem from when we kept a bitch pup of his a few years ago. While she never made much of a sheepdog, she still has her uses. She guards her basket in the kitchen all day, sleeping most daylight hours. It is during the hours of darkness that she is really useful. For, should a stranger come to the yard gate unbidden night times, she explains in very simple doggy words that, should they try and open the gate, she will eat them. There will be no quarter given, and before they lift the latch they'd better have their affairs in order. (Mind, anyone who looks as if they might be a pal, smells of livestock, or generally has 'dirt under their finger nails', can come and go as they like, meeting only a fawning pet puppy dog. Don't ask how she knows the difference – if you know, do please tell; it fascinates me how she judges in an instant.) One of the lads came in early recently, and found her still out, holding some poor rambler at bay in the half-light. This quite harmless chap wished to continue along his way, but every time he reached his hand toward the gate… 'Gggrrrrrrr'. He had to be let in to continue along his legitimate way.

Indeed, it is because of her further interests in the taste of anything clad in boretex designer hiking clothing, or clutching telescopic aluminium walking poles, or riding mountain bikes, that she subsequently spends all daylight hours safely indoors. Oh, and she has an equal fascination for the taste of any canine which looks as if it might not work/hunt for a living.

And so, with Gyp having been to visit the vet for the unkindest cut of all, and the only other young bitch we kept from him going under a wheel at 12 months, I had no choice – if I wanted to continue the line – but to breed from this choice creature. Putting her to a nice local dog – in exchange for some shearing – has left me with a very friendly yearling bitch we called Fly.

And boy does Fly want to help. If left to her own devices for five minutes she'll gather all the sheep within sight, helpfully piling them into the corner of a field. She has so much energy she hardly knows what to do with herself; and because of her hard-wired sheep interests spends quite a lot of her time on a chain, which only exacerbates things. At least now winter feeding is upon us she's discovered riding with me in the tractor cab. Oh but how she loves this new activity!

This is where Gyp has his problem. You see, sitting beside me mornings is his job. It is our own quiet time together. If I wish to point out something of interest, or seek the paw of sympathy when my morning is going pear-shaped, it is to Gyp I turn. Likewise, he can rest his head on my knee, and look up with baleful eyes when he has some worry or other. But now we're sharing our space with this bouncing buffoon, who understands none of the subtle rules of travelling in the tractor cab. From the moment we set off, when Granddad Gyp has to take a moment to think about jumping up, swaying back on his haunches and mentally saying 'One, two, three....', Miss Banana Brains has leapt in and out of the cab three times, tracking mud everywhere. Gyp is not happy with this arrangement. They have also had sharp words about who keeps the seat warm while I'm out destringing a bale. When my boy John was a pup, and Gyp was younger, they too had to have this discussion, and there was a bit of a fight. Gyp won, but only by using his teeth, which he quickly realised was not a sustainable method of career advancement. But now he's a bit slower, the young bitch is running circles round him. Poor old beggar. And while he might sometimes have an effluvia problem, after he's eaten something toxic, she loves nothing better than to rub her sleek body into a bit of wildlife scat, to share the rich hedgerow stench with the rest of us. Boisterous and stinky... yuk.

Still, after the initial round, I get fed up with her stupidity, and put her back on the chain. Then his Lordship and I can continue in peace. When I'm done, he curls up on the seat, in case some task remains. He usually has to be ordered out of the cab at suppertime – or he misses his biscuit – satisfied that he's still, just, top dog.

Mid-winter on the farm

'You can keep yer Rolling Stones...'

Always wanting to compare and contrast experiences for you, I've been off watching some live music again. Starting in a handy licensed eatery in Exeter, Alison and I hooked up with some chums to share some nosh – and take on some liquid refreshment – before ambling off in the direction of the University. For we were to be enjoying that peculiar West Country phenomenon, The Wurzels, at some student gaff on the campus. Approaching the venue, we could hear the support band blasting out an old Jimi Hendrix tune – 'Hey Joe!' possibly. Curiously one of our partners in crime had seen Jimi perform on the Isle of Wight, a 'few years' previously, which rather tickled me.

Arriving at the door, we snuck in without the door staff noticing that at least two of our party had arrived still wearing that popular autumnal scent 'splash of bovine amniotic fluid'. Interestingly, none of those glossy

atmospheric TV ads for Christmas bottles of whiffy stuff feature this odour. I can't think why – I find it singularly pleasing. I should admit that one of the offenders was myself, and Alison had warned that I might not get in. I stuck to the theory that this was after all a Wurzels' gig, and a faint aroma of the cowshed should hardly be an issue. As it happened our chums were, as they say, 'connected', so we were getting in irrespective.

The place was heaving with, obviously enough, students. The support band were crashing their way through some more rock numbers which were mostly hits from before they were born – in fact, I'd guess the average age difference between them and the main act was something in the order of 60 years, which was novel. In amongst the student types was a smattering of more bucolic music fans, including several of the 'usual suspects'. Also, I supposed, there was quite a YFC element, judging from the number of flat caps in evidence.

In the interests of social studies, I did some in-depth investigation on your behalf, by quizzing several of these youths. Strangely there seemed to be a fashion amongst these urban students for such hats, and indeed, sniffing the hats revealed no more than hair products rubbed therein. There were none of those earthy bouquets usually associated with such a piece of clothing. Frequent applications from leaning against a milch cow's flank, walloping an irascible bull across the nose, holding a hot branding iron, or occasionally throwing on the ground when your horse comes in last, give rise to a distinct, almost solid aroma. As my studies continued, one or two of these hats came to hand for various reasons – thanks 'Dan' – and they weighed very little, having scant substance. To save time, I continued by merely leaning over to sniff yet more as they passed – perhaps it is a lifetime of noodles and academia, but the average height of the student body seemed to be just under five-and-a-half feet, so this was easily accomplished. I was nonplussed to find no rural odours amongst the youth within reach. As the evening progressed, I did spot a John Deere boiler suit down the front, but couldn't get through the ruck to ascertain as to its origin. Sorry.

Still, with ample libation, the evening flowed along very nicely. Alison couldn't hack the press of bodies as the main act took the stage, and retreated

– don't feel sorry for her, the 'connected' chums placed her in the VIP area.

I was greatly tickled by the eclectic mix of both music and audience. The niceties of cultural difference between 'rapping' and 'wrapping' might've caused confusion if we could've but heard ourselves talk. Somerset's finest did their thing in the accustomed manner, doffing their dishevelled hats to the late Adge Cutler, and playing a set accumulated over the decades. They're the first to admit they'm getting on a bit now, with a lot of banter on the theme, but dang! they still give it their best shot. With just a touch of help from a backing track, they rounded off with some of their more recent whacky rock covers/remixes, which got the more 'refreshed' amongst the crowd jumping about in a suitably undignified manner. Some of the old fans seemed a bit sniffy about all this youthful stuff, which got me thinking about Adge, and his ethos. It's been a long road, but funnily enough I don't think this is a million miles from where he originally wanted the band to be.

Anyway, a good night out.

Highs and lows

'What are the highs and lows in your farming life?' This was something three of us were asked during the Q&A session after a meeting recently. The other two speakers got in there first with the highs being the immediate and obvious joys of livestock farming. And it's hard to beat, I concurred, seeing a cow nursing a new calf, or a ewe rearing a fit double. A Freudian slip emerged when we realised that one speaker was talking about being present at these births, helping where required, perchance untangling a difficult presentation. Your hill-farming monkey had to admit that he loves nothing better than climbing up onto the peat, and finding a strapping Galloway calf already galloping about after its mother. The corresponding lows are, of course, where some part of the livestock operation goes horribly wrong, which happens to the best of us.

I've been thinking since, and there's another element to this. It's not just the immediate moment of a single calving that makes my heart sing. A bigger buzz, and what brings that golden glow to my mind's eye, is when we hit the end of a long session, and it's all gone to plan. It might be on the farm, or in the sawmill, or sometimes out and away from the premises. There is something very special about working your way through a complex set of logistics, applying differing skills, and somehow making everything go right.

In the mill, this might be preparing a big and complex cutting list for an oak framer. Some might take several weeks, and require forward planning to keep the right-size oak logs inbound, and phasing the order in which sticks are cut, to deliver the right sections each week as the project progresses. When we're really humming, I'll be stretched pretty thin trying to juggle the complex logistics, and getting through a biggie is quite a buzz.

Farming has similar periods of frantic work, with disciplines varying in relation to situation. Up here, there are the overlapping livestock operations at the changes of the seasons. November is often pretty complex, and obviously April brings lambing, calving and turnout all jumbled together. Getting into May with sanity intact is an accomplishment – and one I'm hoping to achieve at some stage in my life.

The author with some of his hairy friends *Photograph by Alison Bunning*

I think one of the highest points was, perversely, the back end of September last year. By patiently watching the weather all 'summer', on stand-by for weeks on end, and being ready when the moment came, meant we saved a very respectable heap of quite edible bales. My decades of farming cock-ups have left scar tissue, but also a small sum of wisdom. And last summer, despite the desperate weather, we were lucky and got through it solvent and ready for winter. On balance, that was a good feeling.

But then it gets trickier still. See, getting through a tough stretch when you've carefully planned and prepared for it is one thing. But sliding through the closing doors sideways, hanging on by a wing and prayer, is much more fun!

If I'm honest, there's a bit of extra satisfaction in having got away with using various dodgy components in the mixture. Utilising the best bought-in equipment, stock and materials is easy, if you throw enough money at things. But weaning a fine bunch of calves or lambs by that young homebred entire is a very warm feeling indeed, or cutting that beam from the shaky oak log with the dead knots you feared would go right in. A little extra spice to getting through last summer's harvest was having managed to persuade the staff to go on using the knackered old wrapper I keep fettling. It should've been scrapped years ago, and indeed, by refusing to give up on it, I presume there's a wrapper maker somewhere missing my trade… but damn! It feels good to have wrapped another 1600 bales with it.

It the littlest things, isn't it?

I should say that someone near to me has pointedly reminded me that the satisfaction of breeding our own replacements should be top of the list. And I suppose I should concur. The satisfaction of maintaining a healthy cut of Blackface ewes, turned onto the hill, is a very special thing. ('Sorry, what was that, dear?')

SPRING 2013

Titles and old cow lines

I must have a smidgen of the risk-taking gene. It's not that I have any desire to leap out of perfectly good aeroplanes, or plummet from bridges dangling on an overgrown bit of knicker elastic. No, the relevant high-risk behaviour is going to be telling you a little of what my beloved has been up to. I'm hoping she won't read this – she seldom does, complaining it's bad enough living with my peculiarities in real time, never mind having to read about it later.

I was originally sworn not to mention the following, so you didn't get it from me...

My lovely Alison was invited backalong, along with a select group of other farming lasses, to share a reception and meal with a titled dignitary. It might've been the Honourable Lady Peabody, but I couldn't possibly say. (Obviously, if there is a Lady Peabody extant, she'll be mightily confused now.)

The rather posh envelope was opened at the kitchen table, as some of us sat about to take our midday bowl of gruel. Reading out loud the gold-edged invite, with the rat nibbles round the outside, Alison rather let the side down by announcing, 'Oh goodie, it's ladies only. Does that mean there'll be a stripper?' After the tut-tutting had died down, I looked over my paper and said, 'Ah yes dear, didn't I mention I had a gig...?'

Alison's guffaws suggested I didn't ought give up the day job.

But then, she'd evidently shared this novel concept with another invitee, because when I next spoke to that farming lady, she assured me she'd be seeing me that Thursday evening. I might add that this lady sounded very much like she was looking forward to it. I tried to warn her that I no longer had a six-pack; it's more of a keg now. This didn't seem to matter, apparently. (Perhaps new career opportunities beckon. Always a good idea to have a few extra strings to your bow, eh?)

Anyway, I understand that the evening subsequently proved every bit the refined affair one would expect. The only Chippendales present would have been finely chiselled, with perfect proportions and carefully oiled and buffed to perfection... OK I'll stop there then.

Now. I've a thought for you. My tribe have always kept a few South Devon cows. They find life up here pretty meagre, this being about as far up the hill as such cows want to lie out 12 months. But they are native, and I wouldn't want to be the man who let them go. As I was leaving school – with a pretty good swimming certificate, but not much else – Dad had been working a Charolais bull on them. He needed the cash flow, and indeed was selling six-month calves very well, but there were only a few of the old girls left. Seeing I was keen, he secured a fresh South Devon bull for to breed some purebred replacements. Although this was over 30 years ago, I recall the bull came from a Farmer Pearce, down at Lostwithiel. We retained several batches of heifers over the following few years, and the herd was set back right. (The only fault I remember now was that those heifers tended to have rather untidy 'vessels', with extra teats and such issues.)

So, although neither Dad nor I were afraid to buy in the odd cow, several of the dam lines would've been with us for some time. What I don't know is just how long. You see, it's very likely that some go back to my great-great-granddad, who rocked up here in 1847. But he'd only moved three miles, from another farm now under a spruce plantation, and there's every chance he brought some heifers with him – his Dad sending him on his way with a few would have been the norm.

We struggle a bit now. The record shows us coming onto Dartmoor 400–500 years ago, giving farm addresses pretty much continuously. We came out of the Modbury and Ivybridge areas, much like the big orange cattle.

Just how long have my ancestors been living alongside this dam line? There's other local tribes who could ask pretty much the same question (and not coincidently my cows and I are kin to most of them as well).

It's not unique. There would certainly be tribes of Welsh sheep farmers with similar roots, for instance. Further afield, I was once meandering deep in the Norwegian mountains, where I met a farmer whose family had been knocking around the same few steep fields at least 600 years. When I asked him exactly how long they'd been there, he shrugged his shoulders, and said 'It is our farm.' He milked 17 cows of his local breed.

I find it a profound thought that within our respective communities there are threads, almost invisible but unbroken, linking us peasant-farming tribes across Europe over millennia.

Curious old world, isn't it?

South Devon with twins

Lactose lovers and the 'working man'

As my boy and I trundled back up the M5 toward his skool after halfterm, he asked a question – he does have moments of clarity – 'In the old days Dad, did everyone have a house cow?'

I thought about it for a bit, and we worked our way forward from the start, instead of going backwards. If we came out of Africa tens of thousands of years ago, into the Middle East, and some of us who turned left evolved a tolerance beyond infancy for lactose – and this is what Eddie Izzard was telling me the other night – are we now in a symbiotic relationship with our cattle? Moving west and north, we encountered country where we couldn't reliably harvest our recently domesticated emmer wheat, but families who could manage a house cow – or goat or sheep if you will – could convert soggy grass into high-value human food. At that fundamental level, where you harvest your crops by hand, you aren't going to shovel clean shiny grains into a beast… you'd eat them. The ruminants we kept lived on the rough, and allowed us to bring domestic farming into the wild northwest.

So back to the boy's question. Yes, in a very real way, everyone did have a house cow. Except, we agreed, it doesn't work just like that, because there would always be some blighter who'd let you feed your cow, and then come and nick it when he was hungry. Scaling this up, and a group of subsistence farmers soon have to provide fodder enough to maintain a standing defence force. Turn the historical kaleidoscope just a little, and the standing army is controlled by a strong man. He extracts the levy to defend the community (although extract and extort are quite similar-sounding words, aren't they?).

Now fast forward to the history of the emerging Scandinavian countries 1200 years ago. While the fledgling 'kings' of the sagas jostled for position, trying to forge what we now recognise as countries, they always kept a weather eye on their personal land holdings and their cows. Their wealth was built and measured on farmland, the feeding of their armed forces being critical. One of the runners-up in this northern struggle fetched up in France, nicking a swath of the coast from the Frenchies. From this base, his grandson managed, in 1066, to snatch that fertile lush country across the Channel. He was lucky – arriving just after poor Harold Godwinson had already fought off one invasion in the north. And this brings us finally back to my boy and me, still keeping cows to pay the rent due to a descendant of the victor. Curiouser and curiouser, said Alice.

Meanwhile, I'm having an identity crisis. I was listening to some trade union bloke carping on last week about the rights and wages of someone called 'the working man'. And I was confused, because he was greatly exercised that 'the rich' should pay more tax, wages should be kept up, and all of those old chestnuts, to help support his mythical working man. But where does this leave me? See, if I've just spent the better part of a Sunday out on a blasted hillside feeding livestock, getting muddy and cold, and adding infinitesimally to my creeping list of musculoskeletal ailments, am I a working man? It sure feels like I am.

But because over the years I've remembered not to spend all my money on fags and lager I've been able to invest in my business and build my rather ragged little empire, and now I'm not sure where I sit in his world. Do my endeavours stop me being 'a working man'? Am I now one of those evil parsimonious bullying bosses? I really am stuck on this one. Although I employ a few lads, I still put in as many hours as my bones will stick, often right at the coalface. And there have certainly been years when, come the tally up at the end, irrespective of no holiday or sick pay, I've been the twerp who earned the least.

When an unexpected rainstorm knocks the farming enterprise for six, or a sawmill customer goes belly up owing me thousands – as happens from time to time – it's my 'wages' that go for a Burton. When some event beyond my control, or even a slightly wrong management choice, erodes my profit margin down to nothing at all, I just have to take it like a little man, and not blub.

Curiously, my union man had little to say about the risks associated with being a fat-cat boss, only seeing the views of his downtrodden brother, the working man. You can see how I've got in a muddle over this.

Brian May on 'being human'

Listening to the wireless recently I found myself being gently lectured by that guitarist chap, Brian May. Ostensibly he was on air to talk about what defines us as 'being human', and indeed, he started off with some very cuddly thoughts: how nice it is to be nice, or some such. Being kind to children and animals was pretty much his laudable route to a civilised world.

Sadly, he then got aboard his accustomed hobbyhorse, and introduced his personal campaign to stop the TB badger cull. Trying to bring as many levers into play as he could, he dragged fox hunting and badger baiting into the discussion, stating bluntly that badger baiting is massively on the increase. His implication seemed to be that anyone advocating the culling of any badger – or indeed, harming any animal – is somehow less than human.

I take very great exception to the BBC allowing him to use this platform to extol such honeyed vitriol. His views may well be well meant, but I contest that they are massively naïve and his statements misleading.

I spend the greater part of my life at work in the English countryside, and am deeply immersed in a widespread and connected rural community, in which I see manifestations of all sorts of human nature. But badger baiting is, essentially, a thing long gone. The last time I came across individuals with an active interest in such things was decades ago. And unless badger baiting is going on far better concealed than all manner of other crimes we see reported week by week in the news, it would appear Mr May is 'elaborating' a point to rally the public to his cause. Either that, or he's far better informed about things going on under our rural noses than we are. And whilst I've no interest in hunting, it is certainly true that some hunting folk I've known have had the most profound love and understanding of the countryside, and everything in it.

I was, by the end of his piece, under the impression that no one should hurt an animal, ever. It strikes me that such thinking is so woolly as to be nonsense. If I give my dogs/ewes/kids a worm treatment, I'm deliberately killing thousands of innocent invertebrates. Does this make me a bad man? If I pick a tick off my leg, or anywhere else, I squish it lest it begins its activities again. Am I an evil man… less than human by Brian's standard?

Will I go to hell if I occasionally squirt some disinfectant over a nasty-looking gash in my battered limbs, exterminating billions of quite blameless microbes?

I've gone straight to the extreme comparisons to illustrate the point. In reality, we are all involved in a continuous series of decisions, balancing what will be allowed to live and what won't. The majority of urban people may be isolated from much of it, but the fact remains.

I've been responsible, during my long career, for the death of millions of blowfly larvae – maggots to you, Brian – through to many hundreds of fluffy doe-eyed mammals. They have met their end because it was time to eat them, or because they were suffering, or simply because they were impeding my livelihood. Some I cared for all of their lives, and loved no less because I was about to consume them. Others I cared almost nothing for, leaving their carcases to re-enter the wild food chain which lives all around me, in the intricate symbiotic relationship in which I am enmeshed.

I consider my relationship with both the animal kingdom and my domesticated beasts as deep and meaningful. I regard the urban masses who consume meat I raise as part of the extended chain (although I think we both realise that the connection is ever more distant). Whether I can continue to balance the level of wildlife and domestic stock around me, as the demands and footprint of nearly 70 million humans grow greater, is another matter.

I've publically said that I consider the detail of the proposed badger cull is flawed, but I have no qualms about the need to cull TB-infected badgers. Like every other part of the ecosystem I live in, a balance has to be struck.

Being human, if we go back to the original question, raises rather more disturbing questions than the simplistic, emotional claptrap I heard on the radio.

We 70 million are stood on these damp temperate islands. Every mouthful of rice, lentils and soya consumed is imported from countries far away, along with every slurp of tea and coffee, and a huge array of fruits we expect year round. We drive cars, cover the landscape in development, and multiply.

The impact of such consumption is rather greater than the life expectancy of a few badgers, and the grasp of such issues ought to be a greater aspiration for, and sign of, humanity.

Moorsman *Photograph by Guy Harris*

Top of the world

One task set before me at this time of year is to count the livestock on a certain area of common. It's several miles across, and rises to a hill of about 1700 feet, taking in vast tracts of lonely squelching bog.

My own stock is found in the first third of my route and, when the weather is kind, it is a matter of considerable pleasure to be able to get in amongst the cows with no other intention than to say 'Hello, girls'. In fact, if I'm really honest, just walking quietly in amongst them is something I enjoy in any weather. And if it's blasting rain down the slope, as long as I've remembered some sweeties, they're all the more pleased to see me too.

There's usually a late calf or two to be admiring, its mother prouder than a proud thing with her new treasure. In fact, there is a bull I bred at large in Yorkshire, who I first met in just this fashion. He was sold untouched by human hand, from an email of a hastily snapped digi pic taken on the top of Ter Hill. I should of course make clear that such untagged, unregistered calves are always gathered in for processing just a few days after birth. It would be fair to say that they seem to thrive under such conditions, and are often very strong 'week-olds' by the time we get to them.

This time I found one group about the same time as I fancied one of the squidged-up sandwiches in my coat pocket, so I sat on a rock in amongst a group of about a dozen of my ladies. Such is their nature that as I sat there several of them ambled over for a chat, slobbering me with big wet kisses as is their wont. It was a very pleasant way to spend 20 minutes or so.

It is true that not all Galloways are so docile. I've recently had an email from a distant pal new to keeping such hairy creatures. While most of them came from homes not dissimilar to my own – his is another bull of my breeding, which dopily leads round on a bit of cord – a couple came with a different mindset. A rather striking red heifer calved last week, saw him coming out to check them, and came galloping at him from 25 yards. I understand that the local A&E glued him back together soon enough, but I rather suspect that the calf might still be lacking earrings and paperwork.

Back to Dartmoor. As I crested another brow I spotted a neighbour, Dave, in amongst a mixed group of his cows and my own. He stills works his stock from horseback, and it was a pleasure to watch a stockman, with three quiet dogs, a good 'oss and fair bit of patience separate out a bunch of his heifers and walk them back to their herd. The unsung level of skill he quietly exhibits is a spectacle to behold. It's only a lifetime of experience, and no small amount of aptitude, that leads to such attainment, and great is the pity that it is not better recognised as such.

I struck off across the slope, hailing him as he was about to pick his way into a jumble of tin-streaming works. We caught up for a few minutes, chatting about this and that, before we both went back to our tasks. By this time, a third herd of cattle had rounded the hill, not long turned out and still marching about searching for the sweetest mouthful. I needed to run my eye over them, and they were headed back the way I'd already come, so back I went.

From them, it was away onto the plateau, crossing the divide between three different watersheds, across the soggy peat mattress on top. Ramblers were thin on the ground – total of three spotted – so it was mostly just the skylarks and me.

Following meandering sheep tracks makes the going easy enough, but they have an annoying tendency to dive off in the wrong direction. Then, and to get a good view across certain slopes without long detours, the only way is to cut across the grain of stock tracks, clambering over great tussocks. This isn't such a speedy way to progress. Eventually, after a vaguely circular route, I come up to the trig point at the top of the furthest hill. Happily, the overcast sky had cleared to bright blue, and the views were spectacular. Aside from the ring of tors behind me, I had all of the South Hams laid out below, with Bodmin Moor to the west, and views far into Cornwall, and the Teign estuary glistening the other side. Stunning.

What I found less salubrious were the bits of litter dropped on this hilltop. Not only that one of them was a slimming drink packet… what? Who could walk all the way up there, and then feel the need to reduce their calorific intake? No, the real wonder is that some mindless little twerp could get to such a point of majestic splendour, only to dump their trash. Beats me.

The 'bullock whisperer' *Photograph by Alison Bunning*

AFTERWORD

Foot and Mouth 10 years on

Not fitting anywhere else sensibly, Sue and I decided to keep this section separate. It includes an outward appraisal of the 2001 outbreak, published in the Western Morning News a decade after the event, and a previously unpublished account of what happened inside the gate, on Sherberton.

I have been watching the calendar, knowing that 10 years on some of you would expect me to write something about Foot and Mouth. And, unlike most things I scrawl about, I haven't looked forward to it one bit. Nonetheless, like a chore I can't put off, here it is. I won't try and look up dates, but just retell it as it comes to mind. Forgive me if I've got it muddled up. I'm sure many of you share similarly graphic, if jumbled, memories.

Sometime in the middle of winter, as the dreadful wet autumn of 2000 slipped into a new year laced with howling gales of sleet, an incompetent swill-feeding pig farmer in Northumberland let FMD into his pigs. As I understand, his haphazard operation allowed pigs access to waste food that hadn't been heated enough to kill off the moderately weak virus.

Possibly it was there for some weeks, maybe not. All that matters is that the genie slipped out of the bottle. It started working its way outwards, into surrounding farms.

One February morning, as I lay drowsily listening to the early radio news, the first media reports came in. Suddenly I was wide awake, hearing that signs of FMD were found in pigs presented for slaughter at an abattoir in Essex.

Being born in '64, I didn't remember anything of the '67 outbreak; only the faded posters seen on the walls and doors of cattle markets. What I did recall, immediately, was that those who'd lived through it in decades past were deeply afraid of Foot and Mouth.

Things moved apace although, as we realised very soon after, some things didn't move nearly fast enough. Many older countrymen and women shut down their usual routines, knowing what the implications were. Reps

stayed in offices, foxhounds stayed kennelled, folks stopped going out. Many farmers took immediate bio-security precautions (which looked a bit over the top to younger generations).

Sadly, livestock markets weren't closed immediately, but continued to trade for a week or so. That single mistake by the Government cost the country untold millions, and God alone knows how much extra heartache.

Here, at home on Dartmoor, we started taking a few precautions, imagining that it was far away, in Essex, and then in Northumberland. I kept the sawmill trading, and went about my life much as ever.

Knowing markets might well close, I took the chance to slip into Exeter with a couple of old pigs I wanted rid of. On arrival, I was informed that the sow would be OK, as one abattoir was still taking them – yes, the very same one in Essex – but that the old boar I'd had on loan wouldn't find a buyer. Not wanting to take the old chap home I phoned the farmer who'd lent him. He didn't want him back (and anyway the boar belonged to another party). So, standing in Exeter Market office, I phoned that other party – a local farm park – and was told firmly to keep away, as Foot and Mouth was now in Devon. Aghast, I put the phone down, and repeated to the office what I'd been told. No one knew anything, and we all dismissed it. So I loaded up Porky the pig, and set sail home. As I drove out of the market gate, I passed one of the Cleave brothers coming in.

Events escalated quickly. Once I heard FMD had been tracked to Cumbria's Longtown market at the top end of the M6, I knew the gig was up. Several thousand sheep went through Longtown weekly. If it was there, it could be anywhere.

And sure enough, in very short order, the virus turned up in Devon. During that previous week, in ignorance, I'd been valuing timber on a farm in Highampton in Mid Devon, a customer had come from the same parish to collect sawn goods from my yard on Dartmoor and, as I say, in Exeter I'd passed within feet of a sheep dealer who might well have been trailing the virus as he went about his lawful business.

Who knew how it got where it did? How many angels can dance on the head of a pin? There were other known connections that I don't feel inclined to discuss, except to assure you they were just as innocent. If I believed for one moment that what unfolded around me was due to someone's deliberate act, I would have reacted very differently.

Once the lurgy was known to be in Devon, we'd started taking things a lot more seriously. The mill was just about shut down, and farmhand Tom took increasingly stringent bio-security measures to ensure he couldn't move any virus between his family's holding and ours. When the phone call came from a neighbour, warning us he had sick animals, we stopped all contact.

As I'll explain later, my turn duly came and went.

Because we went down early on, we then had to sit on an empty farm, watching those who didn't get culled go through a different torture. They had no income, couldn't move stock, and couldn't live their lives. All the time they wondered when the virus would come to their stock. Many suffered the most awful conditions, trying to keep their animals fed and tended.

Farmers who held on showed their backbone. A colleague, Phil – whose lad had been feeding my cows that winter (I'd sent Tom home, so he wouldn't have to see it) – later summed it up succinctly. 'We could hardly let ours go voluntarily, when yours were being taken against your will.'

Others simply cashed in their chips, pleading that they couldn't feed their stock anymore. With a few exceptions, where conditions became impossible, those who happily sent all their animals on the 'welfare' cull allowed themselves to be marked out forever as invertebrates. I'm sorry, but that's how we saw them.

As spring turned to summer, the outbreak drifted up and down valleys, tearing flocks and herds apart. Reports all over the country bore a familiar stamp of agony. Dreadful tales filtered through, with the virus jumping by various means, bringing despair to proud families.

SHERBERTON 2001

I've written this deadpan, as there wasn't much to laugh about. It's brutal in parts, and I'm going to pull few punches, so if you don't think you can stomach it, or will find it too close to home, close the book. I've tried to tell it as it was. As you work through it, you'll understand that I couldn't write it in one go, but had to take breaks to find my composure.

The scene

Let's start at the beginning, if we can pick a point. After years of headage payments and subsidy chasing, with 240 breeding cattle and 800 odd ewes, by 2000 I was carrying far too much stock. I wasn't the only one. Coupled to that the dreadful wet autumn and winter – it had rained 100 days straight that fall, some Dartmoor rain gauges taking 125 inches – and I couldn't say I was proud of the way I was farming going into the winter of 2000/2001.

Aside from this, early in the New Year I had resigned from a high-profile post. I'd accepted what I saw as an honour, but which turned out to be a nest of vipers. I'd been handed a poison chalice, and despite my best efforts I was beaten into submission by a group of individuals driven by ignorance and self-interest. After several months I had no choice but to step down when forced to go against clear legal advice from a top firm of barristers. I'd taken legal advice on my own part, which was emphatic and explicit: 'Get out now son.' Hatfuls of money were involved, and sadly some people can't be in the notional presence of piles of cash without losing all moral fibre. I was sorry for them, but was damned if I was going down with them.

While that business eventually all sorted itself out satisfactorily, this is the backdrop against which I heard that FMD had appeared once more.

The wait

As the risk came closer and closer to home, I'd increasingly felt like a rabbit caught in the headlights. Each step – from Essex, to Northumberland, to Longtown market, to Highampton, to an immediate neighbour – raised the potential level of threat. Once it was across the width of a river, it seemed impossible that we wouldn't get tangled up in events. Little did I know, during

the next few days, that his Royal Tonyness was going to delay bringing in the MOD, and then adopt the 'carnage by computer'. He wanted his May election, to secure another milestone on his way to sainthood, and FMD was an inconvenience. A TV camera caught him unawares, having a little joke about it with Herr Schroder, his German counterpart. That moment, chuckling off the anxiety and pain of thousands of decent working folk, sealed his true character in my mind forever. (In hindsight, the outbreak probably was brought under control quicker by the contiguous *cordon insanitaire* cull, but the cost was grossly disproportionate to the gain.)

It's a jumble of days in my mind now – and indeed was at the time. We then had to sit through two weeks while the State decided what to do, and geared up to do it. That fortnight was the most tortured period of my life. With stockman Tom kept at home, I had to get the stock fed and seen to single-handed, in between receiving daily visits and checks from vets, while Alison juggled the kids, the phone/fax line, and her own work around the yard. All the while it was becoming clear what was going to happen. Feeding those beasts was very difficult indeed.

Through both official and informal routes, I begged to be allowed to retain a nucleus of Galloway cows. If we had to clear the farm, then we could house a group of 30, mostly with new calves at foot, in what would then be an empty sheep shed. They were furthest from the infected farm, and they'd be isolated by at least half a mile from other stock, and then if they got sick, so be it. I know that the request went to the highest level, backed by some very heavyweight help. But in hindsight, we now see that it met with contrary advice, founded on 'other' priorities. My situation, and others at that moment, was to be the benchmark.

My own solicitor was very clear. I could refuse them entry, although that made me both legally and morally responsible for any further fallout. Situated between the infected premises and the open common, I was in no real dilemma. If MAFF's advice was that I was really at risk, then I couldn't extend that burden on my neighbours.

We all take decisions based on the information we have to hand from moment to moment and the best information I could get left me with no choice.

At one of the daily vet visits I was presented with a large map, with the infected farm in the centre, and a three-kilometre radius circle drawn in red around it. As the local Commoners' representative, it was my task to fill in the boundaries and names of the other farmers inside the circle. We spread the map across the table, and as I applied a biro my four-year-old daughter Agnes tugged at my shirt tail, saying 'Please don't let them kill my sheep Daddy.' She had a birthday that week, but she didn't get a party.

It was then that we knew we had to get the two older kids off the property to stay with Alison's Mum. Polly couldn't leave, as Alison was still nursing her. Both locally and further afield, other farms in similar positions did likewise. The family who lived in the cottage out the back, and who had to drive through our cattle pens to get in and out, asked if 'it' really looked like happening. When I confirmed that it did, they fled with their kids too. I took on feeding their horse.

Every time I came back to the house, the phone would be ringing off the hook. Friends were there with support. Most of the households in the line of fire spoke each night. As friends and neighbours we'd always worked together, although the dynamics of the group changed as events unfolded.

The animals around the yard on the infected premises were culled inside 36 hours, which set that household a little apart. Another household was very 'insular' and we had no communication with them – I tried to ensure the vets understood the sensitivity required there. The rest of the households ranged from one who could only see pound signs, and could hardly wait, to three or four of us who could only see the fast-approaching heartache.

Some friends and relatives phoned with offers of help, although several blanched when they saw what was really unfolding. As I grappled with my responsibilities to my onward neighbours, one – Robert S – grasped exactly the spot I was in, and got a very supportive handwritten note through.

Alison phoned an old friend, Marion, who immediately set off from London, dropping her job in the square mile to come and help with the baby. Anyone coming in or out had to be disinfected at the end of the road.

As the days went on, the pressure built. My quarantine request was being explored, but preparations were still being made. The logistics of culling

and burning the numbers of stock within the circle had to be worked through. Bluntly, it comes down to so many slaughtermen, staff to build and load the pyres, and so many tonnes of coal.

The lack of co-ordination was breathtaking. While individuals did their best, many were clearly out of their depth. Despite the protocols on FMD culling being decades old, certain officials might as well have been asked to design and build a moon rocket. It quickly became clear that the artics carrying the coal couldn't access the farm, so my animals would have to be carted dead to a neighbour's pyre. One of the starkest examples of official incompetence came as a State vet came to look over the stock again in the last days. I'd heard overnight that a cousin a few miles distant was to have his stock culled that very morning. Surely this man was well out of the *cordon insanitaire*, I asked? 'What?' said the vet, suddenly alarmed. I carefully repeated what I'd heard. He quietly asked if I could ferry him up to where he'd get mobile reception really, really quickly.

For all their records – and remember, subsidies were paid on individual cows, eartag numbers dutifully listed, along with grid references of the fields – no one had a clue who had what animals where.

As all this was going on, the farmer on the infected premises wasn't allowed out, and a group of his remaining stock, lying on 'off land', was going unfed. They were soon trying to break out, clearly risking taking FMD with them. Someone nearby started sneaking over each night to feed them in the dark.

Those particular animals caused us the gravest disquiet, as they were officially deemed to be the route through which the rest of us were likely to be infected. While all the wrangling was going on, they remained healthy, and it was two weeks before they were finally slaughtered, still showing no symptoms. They evidently didn't have FMD, but we were being told there was no option, there were to be no exceptions. At least one State vet inspecting my still-healthy stock walked off in tears, unable to look me in the eye.

The cull

We were meant to start on, I think, 13 March, when news reached us that the one farmer who was happy to let his stock go was only to have one half taken.

This was obviously nonsense – he was feeding all of them as one unit, they couldn't be split like that. Without my knowledge, someone near to me parked a lorry across the end of the road, and told the arriving teams to bugger off.

It was to no avail, and the matter was very quickly dealt with. The half measure next door was expanded, and the police turned up here that night to have a little chat with me. I was under no illusions.

So the following day, we started. The plan was that a couple of steady men close to me – who'd both had to shut down their respective rural jobs due to the crisis – would help gather the stock. My valuer and some of his staff were to feed beasts into the race, where State vets would tranquilise them. The doped-up animals could then wander off and stumble about until they slumped down somewhere in the holding yard. There a local slaughterman and his team would go about their work despatching everything. They'd arrived with a captive bolt gun each, and armfuls of plastic 'pithing rods'. That first day we started on the housed animals, including the Cheviots ewe that were lambing indoors, and all the weaned yearlings. Those were killed in their sheds, as I gathered the main lot of Scotch ewes which were killed in the old back yard. During a brief stop once I'd filled the yard, I took a phone call from a happy-go-lucky timber merchant friend in Surrey, checking I was OK, and that 'it wasn't too close'. I broke down, unable to talk. Then I simply had to get myself together and get on with it.

The lads who'd come out to help me stayed over here. On the 15th, along with a neighbour who'd agreed he and I would help each other, we set to on the larger groups outside. This included the mobs of unruly outlying Galloway cows. Halfway through the afternoon, as we returned with the last big bunch, we found everything stopped. Marion had run up from the house, with news that MAFF had phoned saying I could quarantine my 30 cows. Everyone stood around not knowing what to say.

Two years previously I had by chance bred a Galloway heifer with a white stripe down her back. I didn't know anything about Miss Flora's scheme to restore the Riggit Galloways in Scotland, but knew that this heifer was the smartest thing I'd ever reared. She was perfect.

As my valuer gave me the news, I realised the slaughter team had stopped

halfway through her group. There she was, standing in the race, second in line. Without a word, I made my way down through the pens, retrieving her from the chute. The cows I'd begged to save were left in the furthest pen, as if I'd hoped they'd somehow be spared at the last minute. I walked the 'line-backed' heifer up with them, before someone put a mobile phone in my hand. A senior vet at Exeter explained that yes, we had been phoned by someone in their employ, who said I could save my last 30 cows. But no, he didn't have the authority to do this, and that we were to continue killing.

Over those few minutes, my whole world turned on a point. In my mind now, that heifer was the centre everything. Huge weights orbited unseen around her, grinding on that one spot. If I threw everyone out, how would they be able to start again? Where would that leave everyone else? My solicitor was an old family friend, and a very senior man. If he said they couldn't force my hand…?

Near and far, people watched, so where would that leave Tony's contiguous cull? The burden almost bore me to the ground.

The vet in charge on site announced that she would stop proceedings if I asked her to. But, looking down through the pens, where hundreds of dead animals already lay in mounds, I recalled my solicitor's warning about responsibility and – knowing that my hand would likely be forced somehow – I bowed my head and told her to finish what she was doing.

I didn't stay to watch. I was beaten.

The next morning I arrived at my neighbour's yard to help. His Dad had gone away for the day, unable to watch. He still kept a line of South Devon cows chained in the shippen, and knew he wouldn't be able to face untying the bull from his island stall at the end of the row. I helped gather their cows together, as he had helped me with mine. My stock was to be incinerated with his, on a pyre on his ground. He had a good level field adjoining the main road junction, and Dad bluntly said, 'Good. The world can see what they've done.'

A group of stray Welsh ewes from an adjoining common had been breaking in, and it was pointed out that they could hardly be left, so a few of us were sent to try and get them. I was put in charge of the team, now being a MAFF

employee myself, but refused to take responsibility if they got away and took the risk onto another common. A vet came with us, and we set up a stock box on the granite bridge over the Dart, hurdles making a chute up the ramp. The police stopped the traffic, and a slaughterman stood on the riverbank with a large calibre rifle in his hand. If one single ewe jumped over the parapet she was to be shot in the water before she jeopardised hundreds more.

The media were already buzzing around, FMD being big news in the outside world by now. Television crews were encamped on the main road. As Layland gathered a group of ewes on ground adjoining the road on Prince Hall plain, a panel van drew alongside, with the sliding door pulled back. The American TV crew interviewed Lay as he walked his sheep along the verge. An old pal from the Midwest phoned him the next night, having seen him on their news.

A sawmill customer phoned me that night. He's sadly gone on now, but was then a big hale man in his 50s. He had a raffish, slightly bohemian way with him, being as much an artist as a woodworker, although long before he'd been in the armed forces (the Marines I think). The grey beard and eyepatch would give him away to anyone who knew him. I'd helped him out when he was in a jam once, and we'd become good friends.

Seeing the TV news, and reading between the lines, he was outraged. He was very quietly spoken, but furious. He'd phoned to gently offer support, and to try and find a way to help. Seeing that there was nothing he could do up here, he probed to find out exactly who was taking decisions. What were their names? And where exactly were they working from? In little more than a whisper, he finally asked 'Do you want me to do 'em?'

He's not here to say what he would've done if I'd said yes, but I've never doubted he meant it. They never would have seen it coming.

The pyre... entering the video nasty

The following morning (I guess the 17th), with most flat spaces in my yard still covered in piles of dead animals, we had to address carting them a mile and a half to the pyre. Along the route they'd pass a farmyard just outside

the culled line. The owners of the cattle in that yard were just about holding their breath.

With enough on my mind, I'd already warned the officials that the building contractor in charge of the pyre site wouldn't get tipper lorries over the narrow bridges, but they still tried. That had lost them a day. I'd suggested tractors and dump trailers, so they sent behemoths from a building site without checking the width. They wouldn't fit either.

With steadily 'blowing up' carcases everywhere, I asked the 'animal health officer' if he wanted me to organise moving them… 'Yes please.' After a couple of phone calls, I'd sorted a trio of dump trailers for the following day. I'd bought one outright, to hire back to MAFF, and the dealer hired out the other two. With one extra tractor hired, my neighbour and I organised it ourselves. Loading them was down to Alison and I, with Alan, a retired family friend who'd seen a bit of life and could face it.

Alan arrived with a big coil of new nylon rope, which he cut it into short lengths. These he looped onto a leg of each beast, so as I drove the sawmill telehandler Alison could hook a loop onto a pallet fork. The driver on the hired third tractor couldn't understand how we could bear it – my favourite homebred South Devon bull lay on top of great pile right inside the yard gate, having clambered on the heap as the sedative took hold.

We explained it didn't matter to us now. They were dead.

We spent a long and intense day, repeatedly filling the trailers. Everyone was wearing the anonymous white suits.

At the other end of the haul, the pair of 'Aardvark' swingers built the fire. We'd organised a timber grab to load the fire, but the firm with the pyre contract turned it down. TV crews lined up on the main road to catch it all on film. It was my cattle, and my neighbours', piled on that pyre on the TV news, night after night after night. Eventually, we asked them to stop using the same footage.

The fire was lit that night. I couldn't watch, relieved to be exhausted past caring. Layland lit his fire, bottle of whisky in hand.

The storm had moved on, taking the misery to hundreds more across the country over coming months.

The aftermath

On the morning of 19 March, my birthday, I wrote a lament for my cows, which was obviously deeply emotive. It wasn't very neat, and I don't mean to repeat it here, but will extract a couple of quotes I borrowed.

When Shackleton's expedition was months adrift on the Antarctic ice, his second-in-command (Frank Wild) had the task of shooting the sled dogs. He wrote, 'This duty fell on me and was the worst job I ever had in my life. I have known many men I'd rather shoot than the worst of the dogs.'

And then a line taken from a famous letter by Native American Chief Seattle. 'What is man without the beasts? If all the beasts were gone, man would die from a great loneliness of the spirit.'

It was obviously a watershed in my life – and for so many others up and down the country. Of course, there are worse situations: human suffering in wars and famines, and personal tragedies of all sorts. But frankly, that was enough for me.

The dreams stopped eventually. It was a long time before I realised it was the sound of the bolt guns I was replaying in my sleep.

By our actions, many of us revealed where our values really lay. Around me, many friends showed the utmost decency and sympathy. The outpouring of support was humbling. Friends did whatever they could, from leaving parcels at the end of the lane to putting aside the odd Galloway heifer for me. Strangers sent all manner of kind thoughts.

A few others were evidently jealous of the compensation cheques.

Possibly, my subsequent involvement in the project to resurrect the Riggit Galloway might make a little more sense to you now.

Another upshot was that I took up writing a bit more, which kind of brings us back to moving on. Let's move on.

Photograph by John Coaker